MODULAR COURSES IN TECHNOLOGY

DIGITAL
MICR
ELECTRO

PETER PATIENT

OLIVER & BOYD

in association with the National Centre for School Technology

 School Curriculum Development Committee

Acknowledgement

Chapters 12 and 13 contain BASIC and machine code programs for the BBC model B microcomputer. The author is indebted to Alan Paul for his considerable help and assistance in the preparation of these programs.

Note: In this book, the symbol '■' marks the paragraphs which deal with the most important ideas in digital microelectronics. Paragraphs marked with the symbol '□' deal with topics in greater detail.

Cover circuit board by Unilab

Oliver & Boyd
Robert Stevenson House
1–3 Baxter's Place
Leith Walk
Edinburgh EH1 3BB

A Division of Longman Group UK Limited

First published 1987

ISBN 0 05 004033 2

Set in Times New Roman 11 on 13pt
Produced by Longman Group (FE) Ltd
Printed in Hong Kong

Contents

1 Introducing Digital Microelectronics

☐ Words

Electronics is exciting, surprising and seems to affect everything. It affects even our language. The word 'electronics' first appeared in English dictionaries around 1940. Since then, electronics as a subject has given us thousands of new words. This need for so many new words reflects the breath-taking speed with which electronics is developing. The pace is so fast that even electronics specialists find it hard to keep up with all the scientific and technical discoveries.

☐ Costs

The cost of electronic equipment is surprising. It has gone down! The first computers cost hundreds of thousands of pounds. Today, far more powerful computers can be bought for around £100. If motor car prices had fallen in the same proportion, a car once costing £9000 could now be bought for £9 brand new!

☐ New Possibilities

In addition to computers, electronics has made possible new types of calculators and watches, labour-saving devices for our homes, offices and factories, and a whole range of machines from arcade games to medical equipment undreamed-of a few years ago.

Electronics has helped me write this book. Instead of using an ordinary typewriter, I used a Sinclair Spectrum computer and a word processing program as in Fig. 1.1. As I typed, the text appeared on a television screen. It

Fig. 1.1
Word processing with a computer

was easy to alter the text until I was satisfied with it. Then I stored the text on magnetic tape. When I wanted a copy of the text on paper I connected an electronic typewriter to the computer and left it to do the typing while I made myself an ordinary, non-electronic cup of coffee.

□ Letting People Know

For a long time the general public knew very little of the amazing developments in electronics. In 1978, leaders in politics, industry and education realised that something had to be done about the situation. They published and broadcast many statements on the need to help people understand and use electronic equipment. One result is the electronics and computing facilities available in our schools.

■ What is Electronics?

Electronics is all about controlling the flow of electric currents so that some useful purpose can be served. You can compare it with plumbing. Plumbing is all about controlling water flow for some useful purpose. A plumber has to connect together various components to make a water control system: pipes, taps, tanks, valves, pumps. In the same way, an electronics expert connects together various components to make an electric current control system: wires, resistors, capacitors, transistors, batteries (Fig. 1.2). From your own practical experience you know that these components are large enough to handle. Microelectronics uses very tiny versions of many of these components. They cannot be handled directly and can be seen only with a powerful microscope.

Fig. 1.2   Electronic components

Fig. 1.3   Valves and transistors

6

What is Microelectronics?

1948 was the year when electronic components began to get smaller. Until then components were very large. To make a computer, thousands of them had to be connected with wires. The result was an energy-hungry heavyweight. For example, the first American electronic computer, ENIAC, used 18 000 **valves**. A valve is an electronic device in a glass container. It is about half the size of a jam jar. ENIAC weighed about 30 tonnes. It used 200 kilowatts of electricity. It was unreliable because it became very hot when switched on. The first British electronic computer was called Colossus. ENIAC and Colossus were built in the early 1940s.

In 1948 the **transistor** was developed. A transistor does the same job as a valve but is much smaller and uses a minute amount of electricity. Fig. 1.3 shows valves and transistors. Actually, what we see in Fig. 1.3 is the protective case which is wrapped around the transistor.

Transistors are generally formed on tiny pieces of silicon. They are about 0.5 mm square. Because they are so small they are called **silicon chips**. It was not long before scientists and technologists discovered how to form and connect several transistors on the same piece of silicon. This is what is known as an **integrated circuit** or **IC**. Today, a complete computer circuit, far more powerful than Colossus or ENIAC, can be formed on a piece of silicon a few millimetres square. It is very cheap and it can be powered for weeks by the electricity from a small battery. The circuit has hundreds of thousands of microscopic components. This is why we use the name **microelectronics**.

Digital and Analogue Microelectronics

Digital microelectronics is our concern, but there is another branch of this technology called analogue microelectronics. It is useful to know the difference between the two.

In any digital system, things are either in one extreme state or another. For example, most electric light systems are digital. When the switch is in one position, the light is off. When the switch is in the other position, the light is on. The switch and the light cannot be in an in-between state.

It is possible to replace the switch with a dimmer unit. The dimmer allows the light to be set to any level of brightness between fully on and fully off. The electric light system is now an analogue system.

Digital and analogue systems need not have anything to do with electricity. A door lock is a digital device. It is either locked or unlocked. A mercury-in-glass thermometer is an analogue device. The mercury can be in any position between the top and bottom extremes. Most natural phenomena change in an analogue manner. For example, day dawns slowly; light does not come suddenly. A room cools slowly when the heating is switched-off; it does not go cold suddenly.

■ Logic Levels

The word 'digital' has something to do with numbers. Consider Fig. 1.4. It shows the electrical circuit diagram for a domestic light system. The system has an input device, the switch, and an output device, the lamp. In Fig. 1.4a, the switch is down and the light is off. In Fig. 1.4b, the switch is up and the light is on. The words 'up' and 'down', 'on' and 'off' represent alternative extremes. There are similar pairs of words which apply in other situations (Table 1.1).

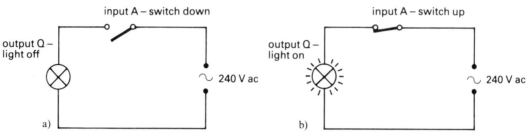

Fig. 1.4   A domestic electric light system: input device = switch; output device = lamp

Because we are dealing only with alternatives we can give each extreme a simple numerical value, 1 or 0 (Table 1.1). The values 1 and 0 are called **logic levels**. 1 is 'Logic 1' and 0 is 'Logic 0'. The exact meaning of the 1 or the 0 depends on the situation (Table 1.1). The use of logic levels is a great help when designing and checking digital microelectronic systems.

Open	North	Yes	True	Day	Front	Right	In	Right	On	Hot	Up	East	Something	Numerical value
Close	South	No	False	Night	Back	Left	Out	Wrong	Off	Cold	Down	West	Nothing	0

Table 1.1   Word pairs

■ Truth Tables

Table 1.2a relates to the domestic light system in Fig. 1.4. It summarises in words the relationship between the two switch positions and the light output. Table 1.2b gives exactly the same summary but uses the logic levels, 0 and 1, instead of words. Table 1.2b is an example of a **truth table**. Truth tables are used extensively in digital microelectronics. They describe how a system's inputs affect its output.

Input A (switch)	Output Q (lamp)
Down	Light off
Up	Light on

a) In words

Input A	Output Q
0	0
1	1

b) In digits

Table 1.2   Switch and lamp truth table

☐ Equations

Logic equations are another means of describing how inputs affect an output. For the lighting system shown in Fig. 1.4, the logic equation is

$$A = Q$$

The equation means that when input A (the switch) is at logic 1 (i.e. up), output Q (the light) is at logic 1 (i.e. on).

There are other basic logic equations which we shall meet later.

■ Logic Symbols

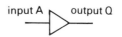

Fig. 1.5   Symbol for a buffer

Systems other than the switch and light obey the equation $A = Q$. One of them is a microelectronic circuit called a **buffer**. A buffer circuit is represented by the logic symbol shown in Fig. 1.5. It is an American symbol used extensively by the electronics industry. We do not need to know about the components used in the circuit and how they are connected. All we need to know is how its input affects its output. The truth table (Table 1.2b) gives this information. When its input A is at logic 1, its output Q is at logic 1. When input A is at logic 0, output Q is at logic 0. A buffer is used to link circuits which cannot be connected directly.

There are many other logic symbols which represent digital microelectronic circuits. We shall learn about the symbols and the circuits and how to use them.

■ Voltages and Logic Levels

Table 1.3   Voltages and logic levels

In Table 1.1 we saw that opposites can be given the values logic 0 and logic 1. In a digital microelectronic system the two logic levels are represented by voltages. The voltages 0 V and +5 V are used widely (Table 1.3). If any point in a circuit is at 0 V, then it is said to be at logic 0. If any point in a circuit is at +5 V, it is said to be at logic 1.

Electronic engineers frequently use the words 'high' instead of logic 1 or +5 V and 'low' instead of logic 0 or 0 V.

■ Making Logic Levels

A simple circuit (Fig. 1.6a) can generate the two logic levels. This is a most important circuit. It must be known and understood. Almost any type of switch can be used including a transistor. When the switch is closed, the output of the circuit is at logic 0. When the switch is open, the output is at

Fig. 1.6   A simple circuit to generate the two logic levels
   a) One of eight circuits permanently connected on the logic board (8-bit switch)

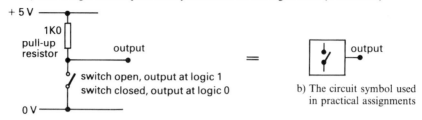

b) The circuit symbol used in practical assignments

logic 1. The 1K0 resistor is called a **pull-up resistor** because it pulls the output up to logic 1, $+5$ V, when the switch is open. The resistor cannot be replaced by a piece of wire because the power supply would be short-circuited when the switch was closed.

There are eight switch circuits permanently connected on the *Digital Microelectronics* **logic board**. Each one is identical to the circuit shown in Fig. 1.6a. Together they make up the **8-bit switch**. The switches are numbered, from right to left, bit 0 to bit 7. A symbol for a switch circuit (Fig. 1.6b) is used in the Workbook assignments when one or more of them is required. This is an 'unofficial' symbol. It is used to avoid confusion between the permanent connections on the logic board and the connections which you, the user, have to make. You should always draw the full circuit diagram in your assignment notes, homework, design work and examinations.

■   Displaying Logic Levels

An electronic circuit (Fig. 1.7a) can indicate the two logic levels. At the moment there is no need to bother with the components in the circuit or how it works. The important thing is what the circuit does.

LED state	Logic level indicated
No glow	0
Glow	1

Table 1.4   LED output and logic level

Fig. 1.7   A simple circuit to indicate the two logic levels
   a) One of eight circuits permanently connected on the logic board (8-bit indicator)

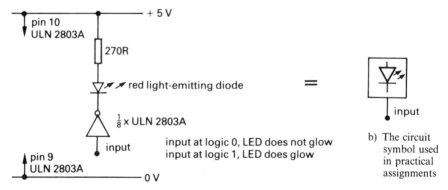

input at logic 0, LED does not glow
input at logic 1, LED does glow

b) The circuit symbol used in practical assignments

When the input to the circuit is at logic 0, the red light-emitting diode, LED, does not glow. When the input is at logic 1, the LED does glow (Table 1.4). There are eight of these LED circuits permanently connected on the logic board. Together they make up the **8-bit indicator**. The LEDs are numbered, from right to left, bit 0 to bit 7.

A symbol for an indicator circuit (Fig. 1.7b) is used in the Workbook assignments when one or more of them is required. This is another 'unofficial' symbol. It is used to avoid confusion between permanent connections and the connections which you have to make. You must always draw the full circuit diagram.

■ Making Connections

A simple wire link can connect an 8-bit switch output to an 8-bit indicator input (Fig. 1.8). The LED indicates the logic level of the output of the switch circuit.

Fig. 1.8   Switch output to indicator input

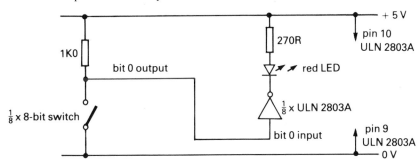

■ Binary Numbers

The logic level digits 0 and 1 are the two digits used in binary (base 2) arithmetic. The 8-bit indicator can be made to display a binary number of up to eight digits. The number appears as LEDs which are either on (= 1) or off (= 0). The 8-bit switch can be used to select the binary number, eg. 1001 1001. The LEDs will display this number as 'on off off on   on off off on'.

A single binary digit, a 0 or a 1, is called a **bit**.

A group of four binary digits, i.e. four bits, is called a **nibble**, e.g. 1001 is a nibble.

A group of eight binary digits, i.e. eight bits, or two nibbles, is called a **byte**, e.g. 1001 1001 is a byte. Always write a byte with a space between the two nibbles.

■ Number Systems

In everyday life we use the decimal system for our arithmetic. The decimal system of thousands, hundreds, tens and ones is based on powers of ten. In Table 1.5a the decimal number 2984 means:

$$
\begin{array}{lrr}
2 \text{ lots of a thousand} & = & 2000 \\
\text{plus} & & \\
9 \text{ lots of a hundred} & = & 900 \\
\text{plus} & & \\
8 \text{ lots of ten} & = & 80 \\
\text{plus} & & \\
4 \text{ lots of one} & = & 4 \\
\hline
\text{Total} & = & 2984
\end{array}
$$

Electronic devices can do arithmetic but they work best when using the binary system. The binary system is based on powers of two. This means that we count in 128s, 64s, 32s, 16s, 8s, 4s, 2s and 1s. In Table 1.5b the binary number 1001 1001 means:

$$
\begin{array}{lrr}
1 \text{ lot of 128} & = & 128 \\
\text{plus} & & \\
0 \text{ lots of 64} & = & 0 \\
\text{plus} & & \\
0 \text{ lots of 32} & = & 0 \\
\text{plus} & & \\
1 \text{ lot of 16} & = & 16 \\
\text{plus} & & \\
1 \text{ lot of 8} & = & 8 \\
\text{plus} & & \\
0 \text{ lots of 4} & = & 0 \\
\text{plus} & & \\
0 \text{ lots of 2} & = & 0 \\
\text{plus} & & \\
1 \text{ lot of 1} & = & 1 \\
\hline
\text{Total} & = & 153
\end{array}
$$

153 is the decimal equivalent of binary 1001 1001.

From Table 1.5b notice that the powers of two for an 8-bit binary number run from 0 to 7. This matches the numbering of the 8-bit switch and the 8-bit indicator. This makes it easy to work out the decimal equivalent of a displayed binary number. Bit 0 is known as the **least significant bit** or **LSB**. It is always on the extreme right-hand side. For an 8-bit number, bit 7 is the **most significant bit** or **MSB**. It is always on the extreme left-hand side.

Words	1000s thousands	100s hundreds	10s tens	1s ones
Powers of 10	10^3	10^2	10^1	10^0
A decimal number	2	9	8	4

a) Decimal system

Words	128s one hundred and twenty-eights	64s sixty-fours	32s thirty-twos	16s sixteens	8s eights	4s fours	2s twos	1s ones
Powers of 2	2^7	2^6	2^5	2^4	2^3	2^2	2^1	2^0
A binary number	1	0	0	1	1	0	0	1

b) Binary system

Table 1.5   Decimal and binary numbers compared

Decimal to Binary Conversion

Table 1.6 gives two examples of the conversion of a number from decimal to 8-bit binary form. First, see if 128 will 'go into' the number. If the answer is 'yes', put down 1 and work out the remainder (Table 1.6a). If the answer is 'no', put down 0 and treat the number as the remainder (Table 1.6b). Now see if 64 will go into the remainder...and so on.

```
153 ÷128? = 1 (MSB)    remainder 25
 25 ÷  64? = 0         remainder 25
 25 ÷  32? = 0         remainder 25
 25 ÷  16? = 1         remainder  9
  9 ÷   8? = 1         remainder  1
  1 ÷   4? = 0         remainder  1
  1 ÷   2? = 0         remainder  1
  1 ÷   1? = 1 (LSB)   remainder  0

Therefore decimal 153 is equivalent
to binary 1001 1001.
```

```
127 ÷128? = 0 (MSB)    remainder 127
127 ÷  64? = 1         remainder  63
 63 ÷  32? = 1         remainder  31
 31 ÷  16? = 1         remainder  15
 15 ÷   8? = 1         remainder   7
  7 ÷   4? = 1         remainder   3
  3 ÷   2? = 1         remainder   1
  1 ÷   1? = 1 (LSB)   remainder   0

Therefore decimal 127 is equivalent
to binary 0111 1111.
```

a) Decimal system

b) Binary system

Table 1.6   Converting a number from decimal to binary form

Using Light-emitting Diodes

A light-emitting diode, LED, glows when an electric current flows through it. The current through an LED must always be limited by a resistor in series

13

with it. To calculate the value, R, of the resistor use the formula:

$$R = (V_s - V_f)/I_f$$

where V_s = supply voltage,
$\quad\quad I_f$ = the LED's typical forward current,
$\quad\quad V_f$ = the LED's forward volt drop at I_f.

V_f and I_f are obtained from a data sheet. If this is not available then values of 2 V and 10 mA respectively are generally satisfactory.

Like any other diode, a light-emitting diode must be connected the correct way round for current to flow through it. Fig. 1.9 shows the circuit pictorially and diagrammatically. The LED's cathode lead is next to a small 'flat' on its body. The cathode has to be electrically more negative than the anode for current to flow through the LED to make it glow. Reverse connection or overheating when soldering may destroy the LED. Omission of the current-limiting series resistor will certainly destroy it.

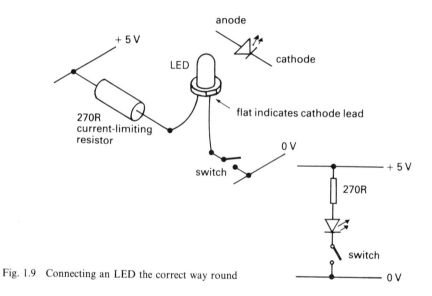

Fig. 1.9   Connecting an LED the correct way round

In Fig. 1.9, notice that the LED glows when the switch is closed. What happens is that the switch connects the cathode of the LED to 0 V. Current then flows from the +5 V or logic 1 level, through the LED and down to the 0 V or logic 0 level. This method of turning things on is used widely. It must be known and understood. Almost any type of switch can be used, including a transistor.

☐   **Historical Background**

Digital microelectronics is a modern technology but it uses ideas which originate in the centuries-old study of logic. The first known study of logic was made by the Greek philosopher Aristotle (384–322 BC). He wrote his thoughts in his treatise *De Interpretatione*.

The science of logic was significantly advanced by the English mathematician Professor George Simon Boole (1815–1864). In 1854 Boole published a treatise entitled *A Mathematical Analysis of Logic*. Boole had studied the work of Aristotle and from it he developed the mathematical form of reasoning called Boolean algebra. Boole originated the logic levels of 0 and 1, truth tables, the general logic equations and various logic relationships, such as AND, OR and NOT, which will be discussed in later chapters.

George Boole's work lay dormant for nearly a century. Meanwhile, the telephone was invented and began to be installed in homes, offices and factories in ever increasing numbers. When a telephone call was made, the caller's and the receiver's telephones were manually connected by operators working at switchboards in telephone exchanges. This became an increasingly slow and unreliable process as the volume of telephone traffic increased. The solution to the problem was to build automatic telephone exchanges.

An automatic telephone exchange is no more than a big box full of switches which open or close as telephone numbers are dialled. Provided the right switches open or close, any telephone can be connected to any other telephone. However, the design of these very complex switching systems presented great problems. The vital clue came in an article called *A Symbolic Analysis of Relay and Switching Circuits*. It was published in 1938 by Claude B. Shannon. In the article he explained how Boolean algebra could be used to describe the operation of telephone switching equipment. People were quick to appreciate that what applied to the design of telephone exchanges applied also to the design of any electrical or non-electrical control system for equipment used in the home, factory or office.

The work of Boole and Shannon is at the heart of computer design. Even though every year brings new and better components for building computers, the ideas behind them remain the same.

2 The Logical Relationships AND and OR

■ Decisions

Without being aware of it, all of us use logic levels many times a day. We use them when we make decisions, for example, in solving this problem:

'If it is a week day in term time and if I am aged between 5 and 16 and if am not unwell, I have to get up at 7 am to get ready for school. What do I do today?'

There are two possible answers: 'Yes, get up.' and 'No, don't get up.'

Normally, we make the decision in a split second and without any effort. But what if our decision-making system, our brain, is having an off-day? We can help it if we break the big problem into a series of small problems. Each small problem must require only a 'Yes' or 'No' reply as in Table 2.1.

The reply to each question in Table 2.1 is ticked off. Only if every reply is 'Yes', does our decision-making system signal: 'Yes, get up.'
Instead of ticking 'Yes/No' replies, we could answer the questions with the logic levels, 0 and 1 (Table 2.2). If we did this, the last sentence in the previous paragraph would read: Only if every reply is 'Logic 1' does our decision-making system signal 'Logic 1'.

Question	Reply
Is it a weekday?	Yes/No
Is it term time?	Yes/No
Am I aged 5–16?	Yes/No
Am I well?	Yes/No
Is it 7 am?	Yes/No

Table 2.1   A big problem reduced to series of small problems

Answer	Logic level
Yes	1
No	0
Yes, get up	1
No, don't get up	0

Table 2.2   Logic level answers

To solve a big problem always break it into small problems which only need a logic 0 or logic 1 answer. Use these answers to make a decision.

■ Decision-making Systems

Decision-making systems can be made from all sorts of hardware from brain cells to mechanical bits and pieces. A door lock is a mechanical decision-maker. Various parts must move and match before a logic 1 output is obtained and the door opens. An electrical decision-maker can be made with switches, wires and lamps connected in various ways. A logic 1 output is obtained only if the switches are in the correct pattern of on or off. Then there are electronic and microelectronic decision-making systems.

Whatever hardware is used, a decision-making system must have one or more inputs which can be either at logic 0 or logic 1. It must have one output which can be either at logic 0 or logic 1 as in Fig. 2.1.

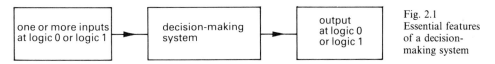

Fig. 2.1
Essential features of a decision-making system

■ The AND Relationship

Fig. 2.2 shows two switches controlling a lamp. The switches are the inputs and the lamp is the output. The switches are **in series** with each other. The electric current has to pass through switch A AND switch B to reach the lamp. As each switch has two positions, up and down, there are four possible combinations of switch position. These are shown in Fig. 2.2. Fig. 2.2d shows the only switch positions which allow the lamp to light.

Fig. 2.2   Two switches control a lamp

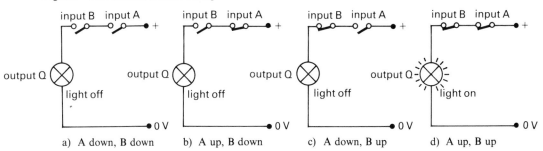

a) A down, B down   b) A up, B down   c) A down, B up   d) A up, B up

The truth table (Table 2.3a) summarises the information given in Fig. 2.2. Table 2.3b is the same truth table but 'Down' and 'Off' have been replaced by logic 0, while 'Up' and 'On' have been replaced by logic 1.

Related fig.	Switches input		Lamp output
	B	A	Q
Fig. 2.2a)	Down	Down	Light off
Fig. 2.2b)	Down	Up	Light off
Fig. 2.2c)	Up	Down	Light off
Fig. 2.2d)	Up	Up	Light on

a)

Input		Output
B	A	Q
0	0	0
0	1	0
1	0	0
1	1	1

b)

Table 2.3   Switches and lamp truth table ('AND' relationship)

Fig. 2.2a and Table 2.3b completely describe the lighting system and how it operates. Fig. 2.2a is the basic circuit diagram. Table 2.3b lists all combinations of input and the resulting output.

The switches and lamp are in a logical **AND** relationship. This means that: only when switch A AND switch B are both up is the light on.

Other ways of saying the same thing are:

1 Only when A AND B are both at logic 1 is the lamp at logic 1.
2 A AND B = Q
3 A.B = Q (This is another general logic equation. Note that in logic equations . means 'AND', not 'multiply'.)

■ An Everyday Problem

The equation A.B = Q can summarise ordinary, everyday matters, such as the news that:

'When the car is mended and the weather is fine we will go to the seaside'.

Just as the relationship between the two switches and the lamp is AND, so the relationship between 'car mended', 'good weather' and 'going to the seaside' is AND.

If you find it hard to decide if today is the seaside day, you can make yourself a decision-making system (Fig. 2.3) with the lamp and two switches (Fig. 2.2). Label switch A 'car mended?'. Label switch B 'fine weather?'. On the lamp paint 'go to the seaside'.

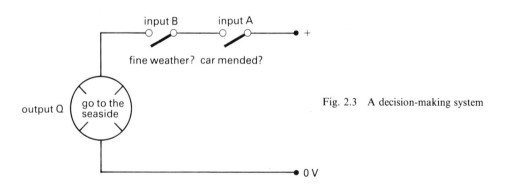

Fig. 2.3   A decision-making system

To use the system, ask yourself each question in turn and give a 'yes' or 'no' answer. If an answer is 'yes', the appropriate switch is moved up to the logic 1 state. If an answer is 'no', the switch is left down in the logic 0 state. Only if the answer to both questions is 'yes' will the output be at logic 1 and the message illuminate to say 'go to the seaside'.

The complex decision-making systems which, for example, help a pilot fly a supersonic aircraft, are developments of systems like this.

■ Hardware

Your AND decision-making system uses electrical hardware, switches, a lamp and wire. It could have used electronic, microelectronic, mechanical, pneumatic, fluidic, hydraulic or biological hardware. In practical applications, the choice depends on what a designer considers most appropriate.

■ AND Gate Symbol

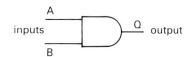

Fig. 2.4   Symbol for a 2-input AND gate
(decision-making system)

When designers are making plans they use a symbol to represent an AND decision-making system. Fig 2.4 is the internationally used American symbol for a 2-input AND decision-making system or **AND gate**, as it is more usually known. Its truth table is given in Table 2.3b. The symbol says what the system does. It does not say what hardware is being used.

An AND gate always has two or more inputs and one output. The output is at logic 1 only when all the inputs are at logic 1.

■ Compiling Truth Tables

Fig. 2.5 shows the symbol, truth table and equation for a 3-input AND gate.

Truth tables are easy to compile provided you stick to a routine. The number of lines in a table is the same as the number of ways the inputs to a system can be combined.

Each input has two states it can be in, logic 0 or logic 1. Therefore, the inputs of, say, a 3-input AND gate can be combined in eight ways as in Fig. 2.5. Table 2.4 shows how this answer is obtained.

If you read each line of the input section of the truth table in Fig. 2.5, you should recognise a binary count. It lists all eight ways the three inputs to the AND gate can be combined.

Fig. 2.5   Symbol for a 3-input AND gate, its truth table and equation

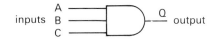

Inputs			Output
C	**B**	**A**	**Q**
0	0	0	0
0	0	1	0
0	1	0	0
0	1	1	0
1	0	0	0
1	0	1	0
1	1	0	0
1	1	1	1

$$A.B.C = Q$$

No. of inputs	No. of input combinations/lines
1	$2^1 = 2$
2	$2^2 = 4$
3	$2^3 = 8$
4	$2^4 = 16$

Table 2.4
Input combinations

19

When compiling the input section of a truth table, it is best not to try to write down a binary count in lines. Mistakes are easy to make. Instead, write the numbers in columns. All the columns start with 0. Study the A column in Fig. 2.5. Notice that 0s and 1s alternate for eight lines. In the B column, two 0s and two 1s alternate for eight lines. In the C column, four 0s and four 1s alternate for eight lines. If there was a D column, eight 0s and eight 1s would alternate — and, of course, there would be 16 lines to all four columns.

The output column is completed one line at a time. First you need to remember the relationship between the inputs and output and the rule of that relationship. The AND rule is that the output is only at logic 1 when all of the inputs are at logic 1. This means that the output column in Fig. 2.5 is all 0s until the very last line.

■ The OR Relationship

Fig. 2.6   Two switches control a lamp

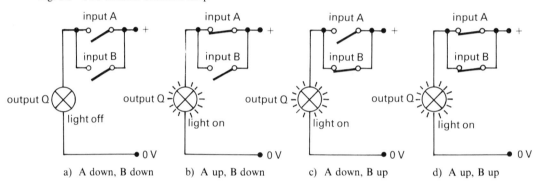

| a) A down, B down | b) A up, B down | c) A down, B up | d) A up, B up |

Fig. 2.6 shows two switches controlling a lamp. The switches are **in parallel** with each other. Electric current can pass through either switch A OR switch B OR through both of them together to reach the lamp. Again, there are four possible combinations of switch positions. These are shown in Fig. 2.6. Fig. 2.6b, c and d show the switch positions which allow the lamp to light.

The truth table (Table 2.5a) summarises the information given in Fig. 2.6.

Related fig.	Switches input		Lamp output
	B	A	Q
Fig. 2.6a)	Down	Down	Light off
Fig. 2.6b)	Down	Up	Light on
Fig. 2.6c)	Up	Down	Light on
Fig. 2.6d)	Up	Up	Light on

a)

Input		Output
B	A	Q
0	0	0
0	1	1
1	0	1
1	1	1

b)

Table 2.5   Switches and lamp truth table ('OR' relationship)

Table 2.5b is the same truth table rewritten in logic levels. Table 2.5b and Fig. 2.6a completely describe the lighting system and how it operates.

The switch and lamp system is an example of a **logical inclusive OR** relationship. This means that:

when either switch A OR switch B is up, OR both are up, the light is on.

Other ways of saying the same thing are:

1 When A OR B OR both are at logic 1 the lamp is at logic 1.
2 A OR B = Q
3 A + B = Q (This is another general logic equation. In logic equations + means 'OR', not 'add'.)

Notice that all logic relationships, including AND and OR, are always written in capital letters.

■ Another Everyday Problem

The equation A + B = Q can summarise ordinary, everyday matters, such as the good news that:

'You can have fish or chips or both, just as you like.'

Just as the relationship between the two switches and the lamp is inclusive OR, so the relationship between fish and chips and you is inclusive OR. An *exclusive* OR relationship would be be 'You can have fish or chips but not both'!

The lamp and two switches (Fig. 2.6) can be used as a simple information system which will tell you what you are allowed to eat (Fig 2.7). Label switch A 'can I have fish?'. Label switch B 'can I have chips?'. Paint the word 'yes' on the lamp. As each switch is moved in turn to the logic 1 state, the output will move to the logic 1 state, i.e. the lamp will illuminate the word 'yes'. Best of all, if both switches are at logic 1, 'yes' is still signalled!

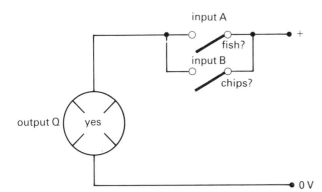

Fig. 2.7 An information system

The OR system just considered uses electrical hardware. As with the AND system, totally different hardware could be used.

■ OR Gate Symbol

Fig. 2.8 is the symbol for a 2-input OR decision-making system or **OR gate**.

An OR gate always has two or more inputs and one output. The output is at logic 1 if one or more of the inputs is at logic 1. Fig. 2.9 shows the symbol, truth table and equation for a 3-input OR gate.

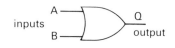

Fig. 2.8 Symbol for a 2-input OR gate (decision-making system)

Fig. 2.9 Symbol for a 3-input OR gate, its truth table and equation

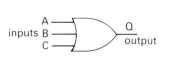

Inputs			Output
C	**B**	**A**	**Q**
0	0	0	0
0	0	1	1
0	1	0	1
0	1	1	1
1	0	0	1
1	0	1	1
1	1	0	1
1	1	1	1

$$A + B + C = Q$$

■ Integrated Circuits

In digital microelectronics, electronic logic circuits are used as decision-making systems. Each circuit uses minute resistors, diodes and transistors formed and connected on a tiny piece of silicon. This type of circuit is an **integrated circuit** and is popularly known as a **silicon chip** (Fig 2.10). There are chips designed to obey the AND and OR rules.

Fig. 2.10
The rectangular area in the middle of the picture is an integrated circuit

An integrated circuit is encapsulated in a rectangular plastic or ceramic package. The package has two lines of metal pins protruding from its long edges. This kind of package is called a **dual-in-line (DIL)** package (Fig. 2.11). Very fine wires inside the package connect the integrated circuit to the pins. The pins themselves enable connections to be made to other electronic devices. The number of pins on a package depends on the requirements of the integrated circuit. Some have only six pins, others have over 40 pins. Occasionally a package has more pins than the integrated circuit needs. The spare pins are not electrically connected inside or outside the package.

Fig. 2.11 A dual-in-line (DIL) integrated circuit package

■ Finding Pin 1

On the top surface of all integrated circuit packages there is a notch or a dot or a figure '1' to help the user find pin 1, as in Fig. 2.12. Pin 1 is always 'top left' and the pin numbering is always anticlockwise.

Fig. 2.12 Finding pin 1

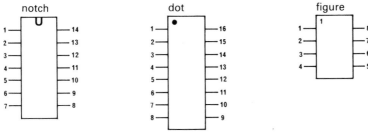

■ Code Numbers

There are thousands of different integrated circuits and each one is designed to meet a particular need. All of them are identified by a code number printed on the top of the package. Sometimes there are several sets of numbers. With a little experience, it is easy to pick out the code number. Frequently there are letters before or after a code number, e.g. NE555V. The letters in front of the number identify the manufacturer and may be ignored. The letters after the number give information about the integrated circuit which may be important only in some applications.

■ Logic Circuit Families

There are two main families of digital microelectronic logic integrated circuits. One family is called CMOS. CMOS stands for Complementary Metal Oxide Semiconductor. The other family is called TTL. TTL stands for Transistor-Transistor Logic. Both families have several hundred members and both offer identical decision-making facilities. They differ in the way they are designed, made and used. Both families are used extensively in industry. TTL devices are found in all the popular personal microcomputers such as the BBC computer and the Spectrum. TTL devices are used on the logic board.

CMOS integrated logic circuits generally have four-figure code numbers which start with 4, e.g. 4001. Standard TTL integrated circuits use four or five-figure code numbers which start with 74 or, sometimes, 54, e.g. 7400. There are other versions of TTL. They are identified by letters within the code number, e.g. 74LS00. Standard TTL is a very convenient range of integrated circuits with which to learn digital microelectronics and this book is based on it.

■ Data Sheets

Manufacturers publish data sheets and books which describe what their integrated circuits do and how they should be used. The information always includes a **pin-out diagram**. This shows the electronic purpose or logic function of each pin on the dual-in-line package.

Fig. 2.13   Pin-out diagrams

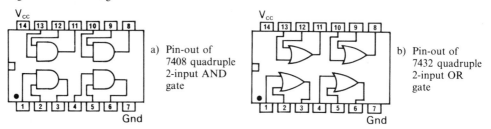

a) Pin-out of 7408 quadruple 2-input AND gate

b) Pin-out of 7432 quadruple 2-input OR gate

Fig. 2.13 shows the pin-out of two TTL logic integrated circuits. Each DIL package contains four separate logic gates — hence 'quadruple' or 'quad' for short. The symbols show that the package with the code number 7408 contains 2-input AND gates. The 7432 package contains 2-input OR gates. In both pin-out diagrams, pins 1 and 2, 4 and 5, 9 and 10, 12 and 13 are gate inputs. Pins 3, 6, 8 and 11 are gate outputs. Of course, the inputs and output used must match.

All integrated circuits need an electricity supply to enable them to function. In Fig. 2.13, pin 14, marked V_{cc}, is connected to the $+5$ V rail of the power supply while pin 7, marked Gnd, is connected to the 0 V rail of the power supply.

24

■ Test Circuits

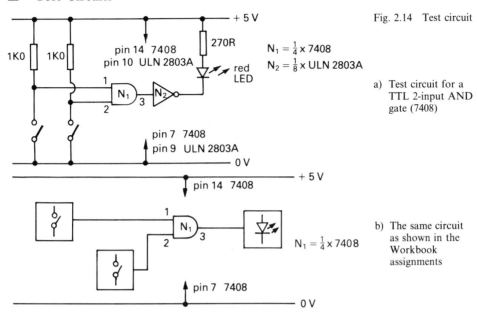

Fig. 2.14   Test circuit

$N_1 = \frac{1}{4} \times 7408$

$N_2 = \frac{1}{8} \times ULN\ 2803A$

a) Test circuit for a
TTL 2-input AND
gate (7408)

$N_1 = \frac{1}{4} \times 7408$

b) The same circuit
as shown in the
Workbook
assignments

Fig. 2.14 and Fig. 2.15 show simple test circuits for a TTL 2-input AND gate and a TTL 2-input OR gate. The gate inputs are controlled by outputs from the 8-bit switch. The 8-bit indicator displays the logic level of the gate output. The truth tables given in Table 2.3b and Table 2.5b apply to these circuits.

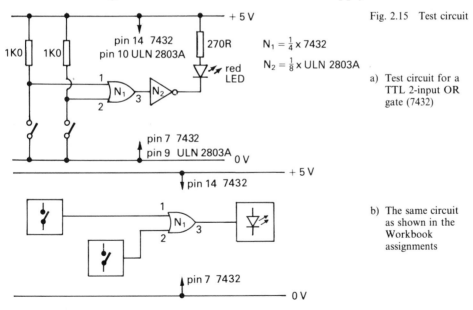

Fig. 2.15   Test circuit

$N_1 = \frac{1}{4} \times 7432$

$N_2 = \frac{1}{8} \times ULN\ 2803A$

a) Test circuit for a
TTL 2-input OR
gate (7432)

b) The same circuit
as shown in the
Workbook
assignments

In simple test circuits, unused TTL inputs may be left unconnected. Under no circumstances should outputs, whether used or unused, be connected together.

25

3 The Logical Relationships NOT, NAND and NOR

Some more very useful logic gates are the NOT, NAND and NOR gates.

◼ The NOT Gate (Inverter)

A **NOT gate** is a decision-making device. It has one input and one output. The output logic level is always the opposite of the input logic level. If the input is at logic 1, the output is at logic 0 and vice versa. The NOT gate is like a see-saw which always has one end up and the other end down. A NOT gate is also called an **inverter** or an **inverting buffer**.

Fig. 3.1 The NOT gate (inverter)

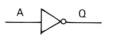

a) Symbol for a NOT gate (inverter)

$$A = \bar{Q}$$

d) Logic equation for an inverter

Input	Output
A	Q
0	1
1	0

b) Truth table for a NOT gate (inverter)

Input	Output
A	Q
0	0
1	1

c) Truth table for an ordinary, non-inverting buffer

The symbol and truth table for an inverter are given in Fig. 3.1a and b. This symbol is similar to the buffer symbol shown in Fig. 1.5. The difference between the two symbols is the small circle on the output of the inverter. This is a **negation** or **NOT symbol**. It means that, for a given input, the output is the opposite of what one would expect from the ordinary or **non-inverting buffer** (Fig. 3.1c).

In the logic equation (Fig. 3.1d) the **bar** over the Q means 'NOT'. The equation is pronounced 'A equals Q-bar' or 'A equals NOT Q'. The equation says that when A is at logic 1, Q is not. It is at logic 0 and vice versa.

◼ Inverter Chips

The NOT gate on the logic board is the 7414 hex inverter (Fig. 3.2). The word **hex** means there are six separate inverters in the DIL package. The 7414 has **Schmitt trigger inputs**. This means that the inputs have special, very useful electronic properties. These are explained in Chapter 4. Several other TTL

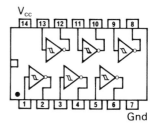

Fig. 3.2 Pin-out of 7414 hex inverter with Schmitt trigger inputs

26

integrated circuits have Schmitt trigger inputs. These chips are easily identified because the Schmitt symbol ($\curlywedge$) is included in their pin-out drawing as in Fig. 3.2.

There is a number of inverters in the TTL family. You should use only the 7414 until you are more experienced in microelectronics.

■ **Test Circuit**

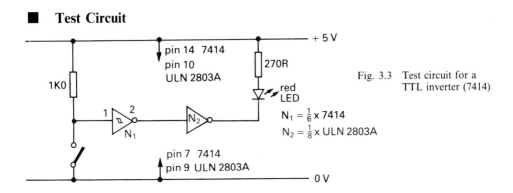

Fig. 3.3 Test circuit for a TTL inverter (7414)

$N_1 = \frac{1}{6} \times 7414$

$N_2 = \frac{1}{8} \times ULN\ 2803A$

Fig. 3.3 shows a test circuit for an inverter. If you study the circuit diagram you will see that the ULN 2803A chip, which forms part of the 8-bit indicator, also contains inverters. There are eight of them and they are used to drive the eight red LEDs.

☐ **Combinational Logic**

Combinational logic is the name for a system in which different logic gates are connected together. Fig. 3.4a shows an AND gate with its output connected to the input of an inverter. The inputs to this combination are A and B and the output is Q. In the middle is C. C is both the output of the AND gate and the input to the NOT gate.

In a combined system, the way the inputs affect the output can be found from a truth table. The truth table details each part of the system as in Fig. 3.4b. Columns A and B give all possible combinations of the two inputs. The AND relationship of inputs A and B and output C is detailed in column C. The NOT relationship of input C and output Q is detailed in column Q.

Fig. 3.4 Logic gates combined

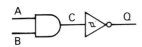

a) AND gate and inverter connected

b) Truth table for the system

System inputs			System output
B	A	C	Q
0	0	0	1
0	1	0	1
1	0	0	1
1	1	1	0

When the truth table has been completed, the way A and B affect Q is found by reading the system input and the system output columns. All in-between columns are ignored.

The system shown in Fig. 3.4a is an **AND-NOT** system. This is usually called a **NAND gate**.

■ The NAND Gate

A NAND gate is a decision-making device which has two or more inputs and one output. If all of the inputs are at logic 1, the output is at logic 0. If one or more of the inputs is at logic 0, the output is at logic 1.

A NAND gate has the symbol shown in Fig. 3.5a. This is an AND symbol with a negation circle added to the output. It says that the output, Q, is always the **complement**, i.e. opposite, of what you would expect from an AND gate with the same inputs.

Fig. 3.5   The NAND gate

A _____⊐D⊸ Q
B _____

a) Symbol for a 2-input NAND gate

$$A.B = \bar{Q}$$

c) Logic equation for a 2-input
    NAND gate

Inputs		Output
B	**A**	**Q**
0	0	1
0	1	1
1	0	1
1	1	0

b) Truth table for a 2-input NAND gate

Fig. 3.5b is the truth table for a 2-input NAND gate and Fig. 3.5c is its logic equation. The equation is pronounced 'A AND B equals Q-bar' or 'A AND B equals NOT Q'. It means that when A AND B are both at logic 1, Q is not. It is at logic 0.

■ NAND Gate Pin-out

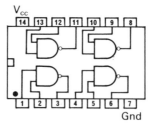

Fig. 3.6
Pin-out of
7400 quadruple
2-input NAND
gate

Instead of combining separate chips to obtain the NAND function, a single TTL integrated circuit can be used. The 7400 chip is a quad. 2-input NAND gate. Fig. 3.6 shows its pin-out. This integrated circuit is on the logic board.

■ Test Circuit

Fig. 3.7 shows a test circuit for a 2-input NAND gate.

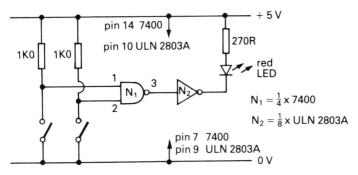

Fig. 3.7
Test circuit for a TTL
2-input NAND gate
(7400)

$N_1 = \frac{1}{4} \times 7400$

$N_2 = \frac{1}{8} \times$ ULN 2803A

☐ Versatile NAND Gates

NAND gates are useful and versatile devices. They may be interconnected to create any other logic function. For example, an inverter can be made from a NAND gate. Fig. 3.8 shows two ways in which this can be done. In Fig. 3.8a, the inputs are connected together to form just one input, A. Fig. 3.8b shows an alternative arrangement. Only one input is used. The other input is permanently connected to the +5 V rail. In both cases, A and Q are always at opposite logic levels.

Fig. 3.8   How to make an inverter
from a NAND gate

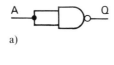

a)

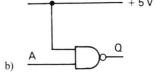

b)

☐ More Combinational Logic

Fig. 3.9a shows an OR gate in combination with an inverter. The system inputs are A and B and its output is Q.

Fig. 3.9   More logic gates combined

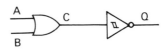

a)   OR gate and inverter connected

The relationship between the inputs and output is found from a truth table, Fig. 3.9b. Columns A and B give all possible combinations of the two inputs. The OR relationship of inputs A and B and output C is detailed in column C. The NOT relationship of input C and output Q is detailed in column Q. The first two and the last columns show how inputs A and B relate to output Q.

The system shown in Fig. 3.9a is an **OR-NOT** system. This is known as a **NOR** gate.

System inputs			System output
B	A	C	Q
0	0	0	1
0	1	1	0
1	0	1	0
1	1	1	0

b)   Truth table for the system

■ The NOR Gate

A NOR gate is a decision-making device which has two or more inputs and one output. If one or more of the inputs is at logic 1, the output is at logic 0. If all of the inputs are at logic 0, the output is at logic 1.

Fig. 3.10   The NOR gate

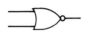

a) Symbol for a 2-input NOR gate

$$A + B = \overline{Q}$$

c) Logic equation for a 2-input NOR gate

Inputs		Output
B	**A**	**Q**
0	0	1
0	1	0
1	0	0
1	1	0

b) Truth table for a 2-input NOR gate

The symbol for a NOR gate is shown in Fig. 3.10a. It is an OR symbol with a negation circle added to the output.

Fig. 3.10b is the truth table for a 2-input NOR gate and Fig. 3.10c is its logic equation. The equation is pronounced 'A OR B equals Q-bar' or 'A OR B equals NOT Q'. It means that when A OR B OR both are at logic 1, Q is not. It is at logic 0.

■ NOR Gate Pin-out

Instead of combining separate chips to obtain the NOR function, a single TTL integrated circuit can be used. The 7402 chip is a quad 2-input NOR gate. This integrated circuit is on the logic board. Fig. 3.11 gives its pin-out. Notice that the input and output pin numbers on this chip are different from those of the AND, OR and NAND chips.

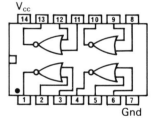

Fig. 3.11   Pin-out of 7402 quadruple 2-input NOR gate

■ Test Circuit

Fig. 3.12 shows a test circuit for a 2-input NOR gate.

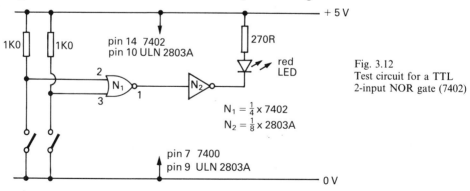

Fig. 3.12
Test circuit for a TTL
2-input NOR gate (7402)

30

The Versatile NOR Gate

Like NAND gates, NOR gates are useful and versatile devices. They too may be interconnected to create any other logic function such as a NOT gate (Fig.3.13).

Fig. 3.13
Inverters made
from NOR gates

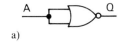

a)

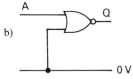

b)

Word of Warning

In the TTL family there is a useful range of AND and OR, NAND and NOR gate chips with more than two inputs.

When selecting logic gates, be careful. Some of them have **open collector outputs**. In catalogues, these chips may be described as **quad 2-input oc**. The gates in these chips need a pull-up resistor (about 1K0) connected between the + 5 V rail and each output before they will work. Open collector chips are very useful but are best avoided until you are more experienced.

Understand Your Chips

Digital microelectronic integrated circuits are a kind of electronic Lego. They are building blocks which can be connected together to make something. If the chips are to be used successfully, it is important that you understand a little of how they work.

TTL Input Circuit

Fig. 3.14 is the circuit diagram of a TTL logic gate with a single input.

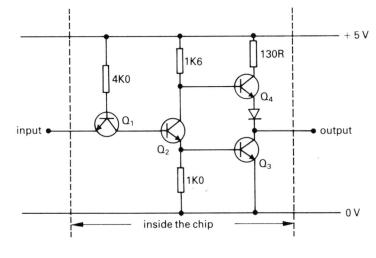

Fig. 3.14
Circuit diagram
of a TTL logic
gate with a single
input

Fig. 3.15 shows the TTL input connected to one of the 8-bit switch circuits. With the switch open, the emitter of transistor Q_1 is pulled up to logic 1 by the 1K0 pull-up resistor (Fig. 3.15a). No current flows through the resistor or the emitter.

With the switch closed, the emitter of transistor Q_1 is pulled down to logic 0 (Fig. 3.15b). In this state, current is able to flow from the emitter, *out* of the input pin and down to the 0 V rail of the power supply.

It is important to remember that a TTL input in the logic 0 state is a **current source**. This is because current flows out of the input pin to the 0 V rail. It is essential that any device which pulls a TTL input to logic 0 allows this current to flow freely. Normally, resistors are never put in its path. For most standard TTL logic chips the current is 1.6 mA.

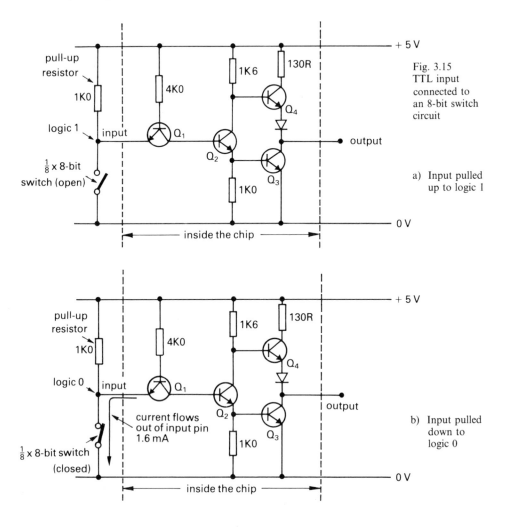

Fig. 3.15
TTL input
connected to
an 8-bit switch
circuit

a) Input pulled up to logic 1

b) Input pulled down to logic 0

Any system which controls a TTL input must pull it up to logic 1 and down to logic 0 in the correct manner.

32

☐ TTL Output Circuit

Fig. 3.16 shows the TTL output connected to a load. The load could be a light-emitting diode with its current-limiting resistor.

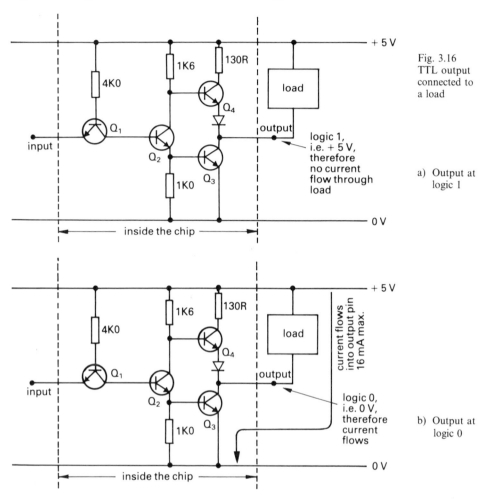

Fig. 3.16
TTL output
connected to
a load

a) Output at logic 1

b) Output at logic 0

When the output is at logic 1, it is at +5 V. This is because transistor Q_4 is turned on and transistor Q_3 is turned off. No current flows through the load because there is no potential difference across it. Both connections to the load are at +5 V (Fig. 3.16a). If the load was an LED, the LED would be off.

When the output is at logic 0, it is at 0 V. This is because transistor Q_4 is turned off and transistor Q_3 is turned on. Now, current can flow from the +5 V rail, through the load, *into* the output pin and through transistor Q_3 to the 0 V rail (Fig. 3.16b). If the load was an LED, the LED would be on. At this point you might find it helpful to read again the section in Chapter 1, *Using light-emitting diodes*.

It is important to remember that a TTL output in the logic 0 state is a **current sink**. This is because the current which energises the load flows into the output pin and thence to the 0 V rail. For most standard TTL chips, the maximum current which an output can sink is 16 mA. Therefore, using

$$R = V/I$$

and taking $V = 5$ V and $I = 16$ mA, the minimum allowable resistance of a load is 312R.

Without exception, any load controlled by a TTL output must be connected between the +5 V rail and the output.

□ Fan-out

With a few exceptions, any TTL output can control any TTL input. They are connected with a conductor such as a wire or copper track on a printed circuit board. Usually, one TTL output is capable of controlling up to ten TTL inputs (Fig. 3.17). This capability is called the **fan-out** of the TTL family. The ten inputs source a current of 1.6 mA each. This gives a total current of 16 mA. This is the maximum a controlling output can sink.

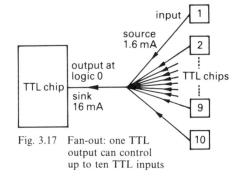

Fig. 3.17 Fan-out: one TTL output can control up to ten TTL inputs

□ Propagation Delay

When the input of a TTL gate changes logic level, there is a short time delay before any resulting change in logic level at the gate output. This delay is called the **propagation delay**. For standard TTL, the propagation delay is about 15 nanoseconds.

$$1 \text{ nanosecond} = 10^{-9} \text{ second}$$

Standard TTL can change logic level around 20 million times a second, i.e. it has a maximum operating frequency of 20 MHz.

■ Power Supplies for TTL

TTL integrated circuits must have the right sort of power supply. They cannot be powered by ordinary dry batteries. These cannot supply enough current at the correct constant voltage. Systems which use a large number of standard TTL chips can require power supplies able to deliver currents of tens of amps!

TTL must have a smoothed and regulated power supply which remains within 0.25 V of +5 V. Outside these limits, TTL will not function reliably and may be destroyed.

Fig.3.18a is a block diagram of a suitable power supply. Fig.3.18b is the circuit diagram. It will power a small TTL system. This circuit is included on the logic board. Such a circuit, complete with its own mains-powered

Fig. 3.18   Power supplies

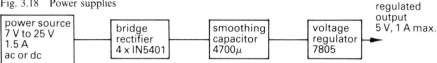

a) Block diagram of a smoothed, regulated power supply for TTL

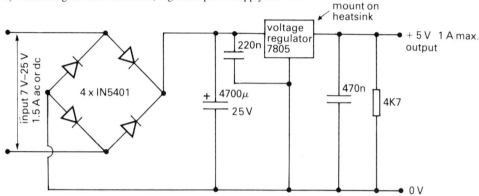

b) Circuit diagram for a smoothed, regulated +5 V, 1 A power supply for TTL

transformer, is very useful for powering electronic projects. The transformer should be able to supply about 1.5 A at 9 V ac. If a portable power supply is needed, a 9 V or a 12 V rechargeable battery could be connected to the circuit instead of the transformer.

The power supply circuit uses a special voltage regulator integrated circuit, code numbered 7805. The current supplied to the input of the regulator must be smoothed dc. It can be supplied at between 7 V minimum and 25 V maximum. The output from the regulator is a constant +5 V. The regulator keeps its output at +5 V even if its input voltage varies. The maximum current flow the regulator can handle is about 1 A. If the current becomes too large, the regulator switches itself off until the load is reduced.

The regulator becomes warm in use and must be mounted on a heat sink. It is advisable to keep the input voltage level at about +9 V. This helps to prevent the regulator from becoming excessively hot when supplying a large current. If the regulator should overheat, it switches itself off until it cools down.

☐   Decouple Electrical Noise

Electrical noise can get into the power supply to TTL chips and make them malfunction. Electrical noise causes very brief but quite large changes in the chip's supply voltage. You can see its effects as the blips and flashes on a TV screen when a car passes, or when a vacuum cleaner is running, or when the refrigerator switches off. Electrical noise can cause computer programs to crash. The chips themselves can create noise when they change logic level.

To minimise the risk of noise problems, always **decouple** the power supply of permanent circuits. This is done by connecting a 0.1μ ceramic capacitor close to the power supply pins of the chips. One capacitor for every close group of three or four chips should suffice.

4 Schmitt Trigger Inputs, Light and Heat Sensors

☐ More about TTL Inputs

To be at logic 0, a TTL input has to be pulled down to 0 V. To be at logic 1, the input has to be pulled up to 5 V. 0 V and 5 V are the ideal voltage levels. In the real world, it is not always possible to attain the ideal. Usually we have to make do with something fairly near. The question is: 'When is near enough good enough?'

Fig. 4.1 summarises the voltage ranges for logic 0 and logic 1 for TTL inputs.

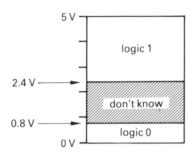

A TTL input is at logic 0 if its voltage level is between 0 V and 0.8 V.

A TTL input is at logic 1 if its voltage level is between 2.4 V and 5 V.

Fig. 4.1   Voltage ranges for logic 0 and logic 1 for TTL inputs

If the voltage level of a TTL input is between 0.8 V and 2.4 V, it is at neither logic level. The logic chip may behave in strange ways and upset the rest of the system. For example, if the system contains a counter, the counter may start counting in a wild and random manner.

☐ Speed

It is essential that a TTL input passes through the 0.8 V to 2.4 V range as rapidly as possible. The time taken should not exceed 50 ns (50 nanoseconds). Such very short times may be impossible to achieve if, for example, the TTL input is being controlled by a sensing circuit.

■ A Light-sensing Circuit

Fig. 4.2a shows a simple light-sensing circuit. As the light level rises slowly (possibly over several hours), the resistance of the light-dependent resistor (LDR) falls slowly. This causes the voltage level, V_A, of the output to rise slowly (Fig. 4.2b). V_A moves from the correct voltage range for logic 0 to the correct voltage range for logic 1. Because this movement is slow, the sensing

Fig. 4.2   Light-sensing circuit

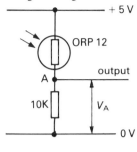

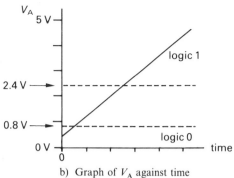

a) As light level rises, V_A rises

b) Graph of V_A against time

circuit output cannot control the input of a normal TTL logic gate. Also, the 10K resistor would impede the flow of current out of the gate input to the 0 V rail. However, the sensing circuit output can control a special TTL gate with a **Schmitt trigger input circuit**.

■   Schmitt Trigger Circuit

A Schmitt trigger circuit behaves rather like a light switch. The part of the switch touched by the fingers can be moved backwards and forwards a little without turning on the light. However, if the movement reaches a certain point, the switch flicks over and the light turns on. In a similar way, the voltage level at the input to a Schmitt trigger circuit can rise and fall a little without the circuit's output being affected. However, if the input voltage reaches a certain level, the circuit 'flicks over' and its output abruptly changes its logic level.

■   A Schmitt Inverter

Fig. 4.3a shows the logic symbol for an inverter. Inside the symbol is the sign which says it has a Schmitt trigger input circuit.

Let the input be at logic 0, 0 V. The output is therefore at logic 1. Let the input voltage level rise slowly. The output remains unchanged at logic 1 until

Fig. 4.3   Inverter with Schmitt
              trigger input

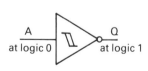

a) Input at logic 0, output at logic 1

b) Change of output logic level
      with a rising input voltage

the input voltage rises to 1.7 V. At this voltage, the logic level of the output changes abruptly from logic 1 to logic 0 as in Fig 4.3b. Had the input voltage level risen only to, say, 1.6 V and then returned to 0 V, the output logic level would not have changed. It would have remained at logic 1. 1.7 V is the **rising input threshold voltage**.

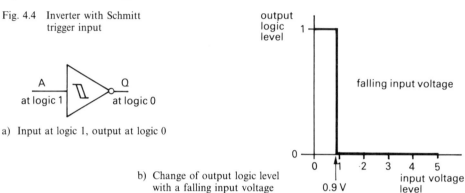

Fig. 4.4   Inverter with Schmitt
            trigger input

A at logic 1   Q at logic 0

a) Input at logic 1, output at logic 0

b) Change of output logic level
    with a falling input voltage

Fig. 4.4a shows the inverter with its input at logic 1, 5 V, and its output at logic 0. Let the input voltage level fall slowly. The output remains unchanged at logic 1 until the input voltage falls to 0.9 V. At this voltage, the logic level of the output changes abruptly from logic 0 to logic 1 as in Fig. 4.4b. Had the input voltage level fallen only to, say, 1 V and then returned to 5 V, the output logic level would not have changed. It would have remained at logic 0. 0.9 V is the **falling input threshold voltage**.

■ Schmitt Trigger Sign

The two graphs, Fig. 4.3b and Fig. 4.4b, are combined in Fig. 4.5. The shape of the graph shows the origin of the sign which indicates that a logic integrated circuit has Schmitt trigger input circuitry. There is a number of TTL devices with this facility.

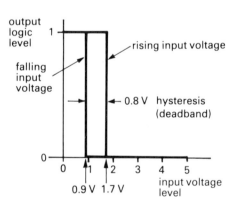

Fig. 4.5   Schmitt trigger input voltage levels
            plotted against output logic levels

□ Hysteresis or 'Deadband'

Fig. 4.5 shows that there is a 0.8 V difference between the threshold voltages for rising and falling inputs. This difference is the **hysteresis** of the Schmitt trigger circuit, sometimes called the **deadband**.

Hysteresis is essential to the successful operation of a Schmitt trigger circuit. If there was no hysteresis, the rising and falling input threshold voltages would be the same. To the output, this one voltage level would mean both 'go high' and 'go low'. The output would do its best to oblige! Every time the input reached the threshold voltage, the output would repeatedly change logic level at high speed, i.e. it would oscillate. This would cause problems with any devices being controlled by that output, e.g. counters would count wildly.

■ Schmitt Your Sensor Output

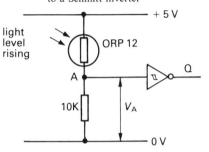

Fig. 4.6   Light-sensing circuit connected to a Schmitt inverter

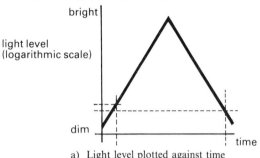

Fig. 4.7   Light-sensing circuit performance

a) Light level plotted against time

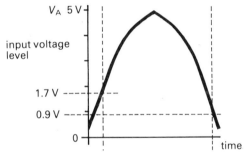

b) Voltage level V_A plotted against time

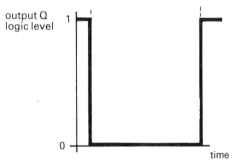

c) Resulting logic level of output Q against time

Fig. 4.6 shows a light-sensing circuit connected to an inverter with Schmitt trigger input circuitry.

Fig. 4.7a shows how the brightness of the light falling on the light-dependent resistor (Fig. 4.6) might vary. Over a period of time it changes from dim to bright and back to dim. Fig. 4.7b is a graph of the resulting voltage level, V_A, at the input of the inverter. Fig. 4.7c shows how the logic level of output Q changes during the same period of time. By tracing from the two logic level changes (Fig. 4.7c) up to Fig. 4.7b and Fig. 4.7a, it can be seen that they occur at different input voltage and light levels. The differences are due to the hysteresis of the Schmitt trigger circuitry.

■ A More Sensitive Circuit

The light-sensing circuit shown in Fig. 4.6 is insensitive to small changes in light level. Extreme changes of brightness are necessary to make output Q change logic level. The circuit's response can be improved with a few additional components.

Fig. 4.8 Switching circuits

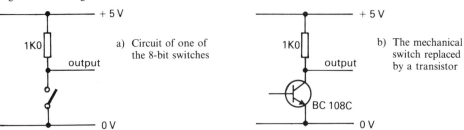

a) Circuit of one of the 8-bit switches

b) The mechanical switch replaced by a transistor

Fig. 4.8a shows the familiar circuit of one of the 8-bit switches. The mechanical switch can be replaced by a transistor, Fig. 4.8b. The transistor can be controlled so that the circuit output changes logic level just as it did when the mechanical switch was in place.

Fig. 4.9 An improved light-sensitive circuit

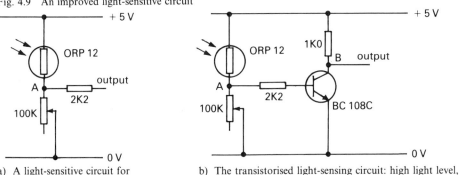

a) A light-sensitive circuit for controlling a transistor

b) The transistorised light-sensing circuit: high light level, output at logic 0; low light level, output at logic 1

Fig. 4.9a is a light-sensing circuit suitable for controlling a transistor. It is a development of the circuit shown in Fig. 4.2a. The variable resistor (VR) allows the circuit to be adjusted so that it is able to respond to different ranges of light level. The output of this circuit is connected to the base of the transistor circuit shown in Fig. 4.8b. The complete circuit is shown in Fig. 4.9b.

☐ How It Works

In Fig. 4.9b, if the LDR is in the light, its resistance is low. The voltage level at A is high. The transistor is turned on. Output B is at logic 0.

If the LDR is in the dark, its resistance is high. The voltage level at A is low. The transistor is turned off. Output B is at logic 1.

The circuit can be made to

Fig. 4.10 VR and LDR exchanged: high light level, output at logic 1; low light level, output at logic 0

40

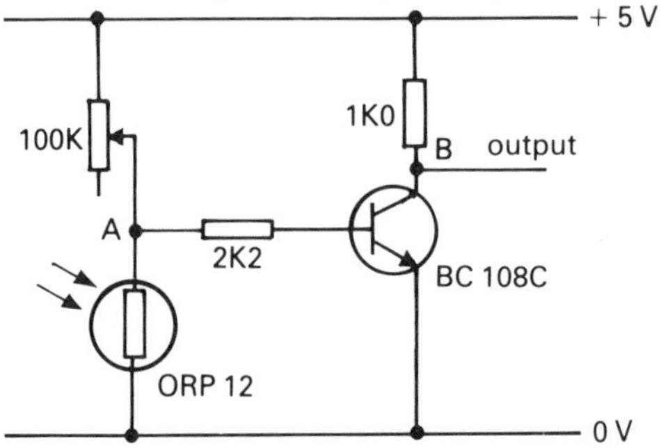

respond in the opposite manner. The variable resistor and the light-dependent resistor change places as in Fig. 4.10.

☐ Circuit Refinements

When the outputs of the sensing circuits (Fig. 4.9b and Fig. 4. 10) are between logic levels, they are liable to oscillate rapidly. A 10μ capacitor connected between the output and the 0 V rail prevents this (Fig. 4.11).

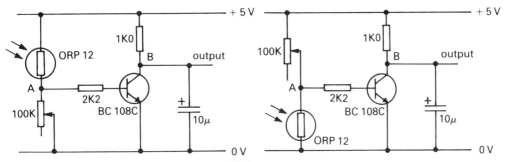

Fig. 4.11   A 10μ capacitor prevents output oscillation

This circuit (Fig. 4.11) is useful in projects. The capacitor limits the number of times per second the output can change logic level. If this causes problems, you can experiment with lower value capacitors.

☐ Output Indicator

When adjusting and testing a sensing circuit it is useful to have an output logic level indicator. The circuit shown in Fig. 4.12a serves this purpose. It is connected to the sensing circuit as shown in Fig. 4.12b. When the output is at logic 1 the red LED is on. When the output is at logic 0 the red LED is off. The LED tends to fade on and off rather than switch abruptly.

The circuit shown in Fig. 4.12b is permanently connected on the logic board. Plug-in leads allow the LDR and VR to be in the positions shown or swapped over.

Fig. 4.12   Output indicator

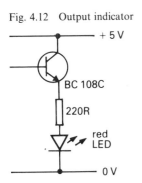

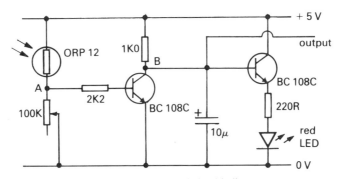

a) Logic level indicator circuit   b) Sensing circuit complete with logic level indicator

Temperature-sensing Circuit

Fig. 4.13 shows the previous sensing circuit altered so that it senses temperature. The sensor is a thermistor with a negative temperature coefficient. This means that as temperature rises, the resistance of the thermistor falls, and vice versa.

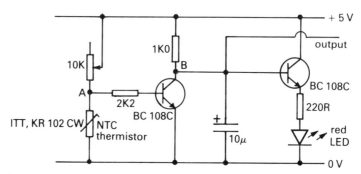

Fig. 4.13 Temperature-sensing circuit: low temperature, output at logic 0; high temperature, output at logic 1

With the thermistor connected as shown in Fig. 4.13, the sensing circuit's output is at logic 0 when the temperature is low. It is at logic 1 when the temperature is high. If the circuit has to respond in the opposite manner, the 10K variable resistor and the thermistor are exchanged.

Sensor to Digital Connections

The outputs of the light and heat sensor circuits always change logic level too slowly for the inputs of ordinary TTL gates. Always connect these outputs to gates whose inputs have Schmitt trigger circuitry (Fig. 4.14). The 7414 hex inverter, with its Schmitt trigger inputs, is one of the most useful chips for this purpose.

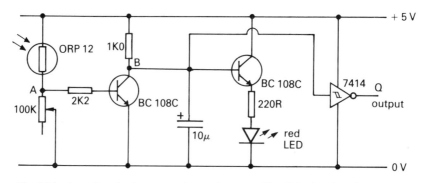

Fig. 4.14 A sensing circuit connected to an inverter with a Schmitt trigger input

42

☐ Circuit Analysis

It is essential that you can work through a circuit and say what is going on. For example, in Fig. 4.14:

> If the LDR is in light its resistance is low. Therefore the voltage at A is high. Therefore the transistor is turned on. Therefore B is at logic 0. Therefore Q is at logic 1.

Try analysing the circuit when the LDR is in the dark.

☐ Other Sensors

There are many types of sensor and designs for sensing circuits which will respond to physical phenomena such as strain, sound, acceleration, humidity and pressure. Electronics magazines and manufacturers' data sheets offer an abundance of information and circuit ideas. Almost always, sensing circuits must be connected to logic circuits through a Schmitt trigger circuit.

☐ More about TTL Outputs

TTL outputs were described in Chapter 3. Ideally, when an output is at logic 0 it is electrically at 0 V. When it is at logic 1, it is at 5 V. In reality, the logic 1 voltage level can be between 3.5 V and 5 V. It is important to keep these figures in mind when checking outputs with a voltmeter in case you discard a perfectly good chip as faulty!

5 Mechanical Inputs and Useful Outputs

Mechanical Switches

The slide switches which make up the 8-bit switch are mechanical switches. Inside a mechanical switch are two pieces of metal called **contacts**. When the switch is operated, the contacts are made to touch so that an electric current can pass from one to the other. When the switch is not operated, the contacts are pulled apart and current does not flow.

A switch in which the contacts are apart when not operated is called a **normally open** or **NO switch**. The opposite is a **normally closed** or **NC switch**. Both types of switch are useful. Some switches are designed so that they can be used either NO or NC. They are called **changeover switches**.

There are many ways in which the contacts in a mechanical switch can be moved. For example, they may be moved by:

> a push-button, e.g. a front door bell button;
> a toggle mechanism, e.g. a domestic light switch;
> a permanent magnet brought close to the contacts, e.g. a reed switch;
> an energised electromagnet, e.g. a relay.

Fig. 5.1 shows how a push-button switch is wired to produce logic level signals. When the push-button is not pressed, the output from the circuit is at logic 1, as in Fig. 5.1a. When the button is pressed, the output is at logic 0, as in Fig. 5.1b. The circuit is identical to one of the 8-bit switch circuits.

Fig. 5.1   Push-button circuit

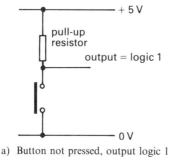

a) Button not pressed, output logic 1   b) Button pressed, output logic 0

Contact Bounce

When switch contacts close, they bounce against each other many times before coming to rest touching firmly. This phenomenon is called **contact bounce**. It is a small scale and very fast version of what happens when a ball is dropped on to a floor. The ball bounces against the floor repeatedly before coming to rest in contact with it.

Contact bounce lasts a very short time, say ten milliseconds. In catalogues of switches for use in electronic circuits, the suppliers usually quote contact bounce durations. They are long in cheap, low quality, switches. They are shorter in better quality, but more expensive, switches. Even in an expensive switch, hundreds of bounces can occur each time it is closed. The result is that the output of a switch circuit (Fig. 5.1) produces not just one but many changes of logic level every time the switch is closed.

☐ Contact Bounce in Detail

Fig. 5.2a shows the ideal output waveform of the push-button circuit in Fig. 5.1. When the button is pressed, the output should move cleanly from logic 1 to logic 0. It should stay at logic 0 for time t, the time for which the button is held down. When the button is released, the output should return cleanly from logic 0 to logic 1.

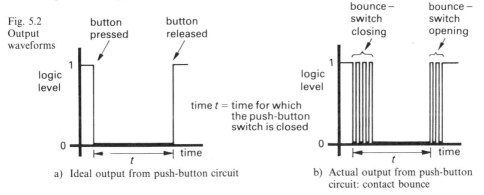

Fig. 5.2 Output waveforms

a) Ideal output from push-button circuit

b) Actual output from push-button circuit: contact bounce

Fig. 5.2b shows the actual output waveform. When the button is pressed, the output moves back and forth many times from logic 0 to logic 1 as the switch contacts bounce. Eventually, the output settles at logic 0. When the button is released there are further rapid logic 0 to logic 1 transitions before the output settles in its original logic 1 state.

A logic gate connected to the output of a mechanical switch circuit responds to every one of the hundreds of changes in logic level which occur during contact bounce. In some logic circuits, such as those in Activities 1 to 4, contact bounce does not matter. In other circuits, it can cause serious problems. For example, suppose the number of times the switch is operated is to be counted by an electronic counter. The counter will increment by some large number each time the switch is operated. What happens is that the counter counts every bounce of the switch contacts.

The opening of switch contacts produces an effect very similar to contact bounce. This is because contacts do not part smoothly in one single, clean movement. This too is shown in Fig. 5.2b.

■ Designing a Debouncing Circuit

The effects of contact bounce can be eliminated by a **debouncing circuit**. One such circuit uses the fact that it takes time to charge a capacitor through a resistor.

The capacitor is connected between the switch circuit's output and the 0 V line (Fig. 5.3). When using TTL logic chips, a 10μ capacitor working with a 2K2 pull-up resistor should be satisfactory.

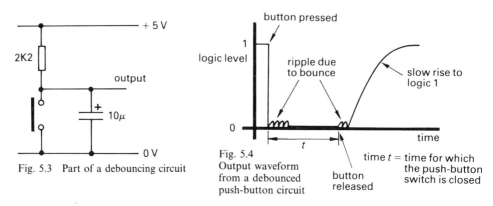

Fig. 5.3   Part of a debouncing circuit

Fig. 5.4
Output waveform from a debounced push-button circuit

time t = time for which the push-button switch is closed

Fig. 5.4 shows the output waveform of the circuit shown in Fig. 5.3. When the push-button is pressed, the capacitor is discharged through the switch. The output moves from logic 1 to logic 0. The switch contacts bounce and, each time the contacts part, the capacitor charges a little through the 2K2 pull-up resistor. The capacitor discharges each time the contacts close again. This charging and discharging causes the output to ripple during the contact bounce period. At the end of this period, the output settles at logic 0. When

Fig. 5.5   The debouncing circuit developed

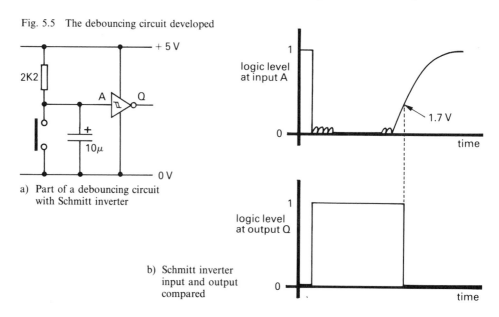

a) Part of a debouncing circuit with Schmitt inverter

b) Schmitt inverter input and output compared

the push-button is released, the capacitor charges through the 2K2 pull-up resistor and the output of the switch circuit slowly returns to logic 1.

This slow return to logic 1 means that the output of the circuit (Fig. 5.3) must be connected to a gate which has Schmitt trigger input circuitry as in Fig. 5.5a.

Fig. 5.5b compares the input to and the output from the Schmitt inverter as the button is pressed, held and then released.

☐ **Capacitor Size**

The value of the capacitor in the circuit in Fig. 5.5a may be increased or decreased experimentally to suit a particular situation.

If the value of the capacitor is too small, the contact bounce ripple will rise above 1.7 V and fall below 0.9 V as in Fig. 5.6a. These are the Schmitt inverter's input threshold voltages. The result is that the inverter's output changes logic level as often as the contacts bounce. The effect of contact bounce is passed on and not eliminated.

If the value of the capacitor is too large, the effect of contact bounce is eliminated. But, when the push-button is released, the capacitor takes a long time to recharge to 1.7 V. This is the Schmitt inverter's input threshold voltage for a logic 0 output. As a result, there is a delay between the push-button being released and the output of the Schmitt inverter returning to logic 0 as in Fig. 5.6b. This may not matter if there are long intervals between each operation of the push-button. However, if the push-button is repeatedly operated in a very short space of time, only the first operation will register. This is because the capacitor does not have time to recharge to 1.7 V before the button is pressed again.

Fig. 5.6   Effect of capacitor size on the waveform at the input to the Schmitt inverter

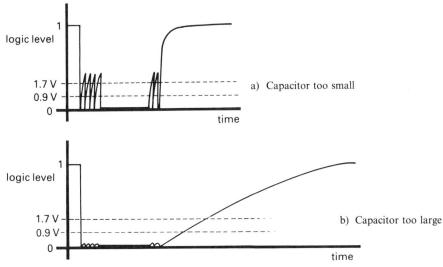

47

■ Final Debouncing Circuit

In Fig. 5.5a, when the push-button is pressed to discharge the capacitor, a high current flows through the switch contacts for a short time. Also, arcing (sparks) occurs between the contacts. This burns them and makes them deteriorate. In addition, arcing causes electrical noise. This can make other parts of a system malfunction, for example, it can make counters increment unintentionally.

The problems are overcome if a small value resistor (e.g. 100R) is connected in series with the push-button as in Fig. 5.7.

Fig. 5.7 Complete debouncing circuit for a push-button

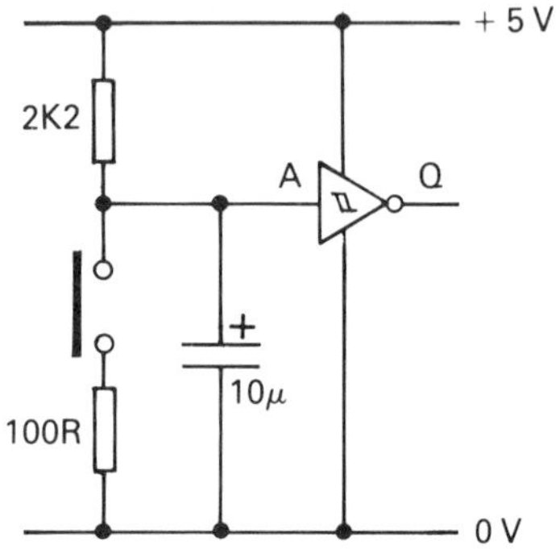

The 2K2 and 100R resistors form a potential divider. When the push-button is pressed, the effect of the potential divider is to hold the input of the Schmitt inverter at 0.22 V instead of 0 V. This is quite satisfactory as 0.22 V is well within the 0 V to 0.9 V range which a Schmitt trigger input recognises as logic 0.

■ When to Debounce

It is not always necessary to debounce a mechanical switch. Keep in mind for later work that debouncing is needed if the switch is connected to the **clock (CLK) input** of a J-K flip flop or a counter.

The debouncing circuit, as in Fig. 5.7, is suitable for manually operated push-buttons and other mechanical switches not subject to rapid repeat operation. Switches which are subject to rapid repeat operation, e.g. a reed switch operated by a magnet attached to a spinning disc, should be debounced with an R-S flip-flop as shown later in Chapter 6.

■ Logic Board Push-buttons

On the logic board there are two push-buttons. Each is permanently connected to the 0 V rail by a 100R resistor, as in Fig. 5.8a. In the assignments, this circuit is represented by the symbol shown in Fig. 5.8b. The

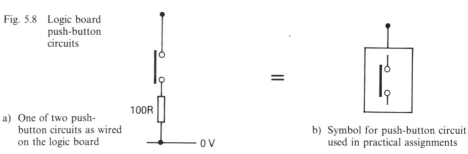

Fig. 5.8 Logic board push-button circuits

a) One of two push-button circuits as wired on the logic board

b) Symbol for push-button circuit used in practical assignments

48

symbol is used so that the assignment diagrams show only the connections which you must make.

A logic board push-button circuit cannot be used alone. It must be used with other components, at the very least with a pull-up resistor, as in Fig. 5.9.

This circuit may be connected to any TTL input provided its contact bounce does not matter. It can be used in place of an 8-bit switch. If a debounced push-button is required, the circuit shown in Fig. 5.7 is connected.

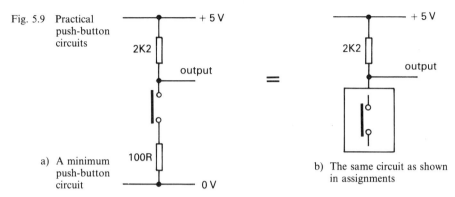

Fig. 5.9 Practical push-button circuits

a) A minimum push-button circuit

b) The same circuit as shown in assignments

■ Logic Board Resistors and Capacitors

There are four resistors and eight capacitors on the logic board as in Fig. 5.10. These components are not connected in any way. They are provided so that circuits such as the debouncing circuit in Fig. 5.7 can be built. Six of the capacitors, 1μ, 10μ, 470μ and 1000μ, are polarised. Care must be taken to connect them into circuits the right way round.

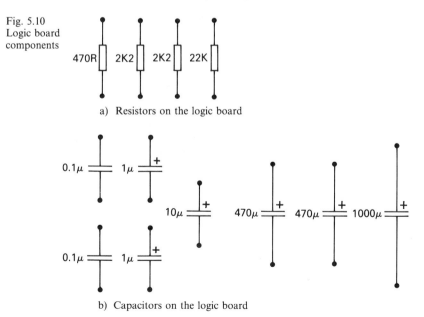

Fig. 5.10 Logic board components

a) Resistors on the logic board

b) Capacitors on the logic board

49

■ Driving LEDs from TTL Outputs

Chapter 3 explained that the outputs of TTL gates are current sink circuits. A load must be connected between the +5 V supply and a gate output. The maximum current a standard TTL output can sink is 16 mA.

Fig. 5.11 shows five logic gates. Each is connected to an LED in series with a current-limiting resistor. In every case, an LED is on only when a gate output is at logic 0. The LED is off when the gate output is at logic 1. The gate outputs can drive gate inputs in addition to the LEDs provided the total sink current does not exceed 16 mA.

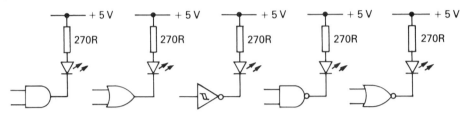

Fig. 5.11   TTL gates controlling LEDs: LEDs on only when gate outputs are at logic 0

This type of circuit is useful if indicators are needed at different points in a logic system. When designing such indicators, you need to think carefully about when an LED is on.

There are ten LEDs, arranged as traffic and pedestrian crossing lights, on the logic board. Each LED has a current-limiting resistor and a permanent connection to the +5 V supply.

■ Driving High Current Loads from TTL Outputs

Logic gate outputs may control equipment such as electric motors, loud-speakers, bells, lamps and printers. The working voltages and current requirements of these devices mean that they cannot be connected directly to the output of a logic gate. The gate output and the device must be **interfaced** with a **Darlington Driver** and, possibly, a **relay**.

■ The Darlington Driver

Fig. 5.12 shows two transistors connected in a **Darlington pair** or **Darlington Driver** configuration.

The two transistors connected in the Darlington configuration are available in single packages. However, two separate transistors may be used (Fig. 5.12). This is called a **discrete component Darlington Driver**.

The circuit may be regarded as a 'super transistor'. A very tiny base

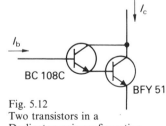

Fig. 5.12
Two transistors in a
Darlington pair configuration

50

Fig. 5.13   A discrete component Darlington Driver

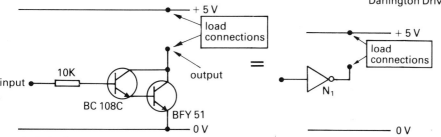

N₁ = discrete component Darlington Driver

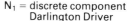

a) A Darlington Driver circuit

b) A symbol for the Darlington Driver circuit

current, I_b, can cause a very large collector current, I_c, to flow. With the transistors shown, a current of about 40 μA supplied to the base of the BC 108C will cause the maximum allowable collector current of 1 A to flow through the BFY 51.

Darlington Drivers can be designed for a wide range of voltage and current requirements.

Fig. 5.13a shows the Darlington Driver circuit on the logic board.

A Darlington Driver behaves like an inverter, hence the symbol shown in Fig. 5.13b. When its input is at logic 1, its output is at logic 0 and the load is energised. When its input is at logic 0, its output is at logic 1 and the load is turned off. It is another current sink circuit.

Any load connected to the Darlington Driver on the logic board, and which also uses the logic board power supply, should draw a current of no more than 500 mA. This is to avoid overloading the power supply circuit.

Fig. 5.14 shows an AND gate controlling a Darlington Driver. The Darlington Driver controls an LED in series with a current-limiting resistor. The LED could be one of the logic board traffic lights. When the output of the AND gate is at logic 0, the Darlington Driver output is at logic 1. The LED is off. When the output of the AND gate is at logic 1 the Darlington Driver output is at logic 0. The LED is on. You can think of the LED as indicating the logic level of the AND gate output. This should give you a clue as to how the 8-bit indicator works.

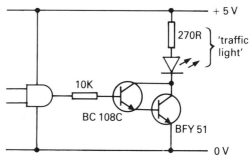

Fig. 5.14   An AND gate controlling a Darlington Driver which controls an LED

■ Relays

A relay is a switch whose contacts move when a current passes through the coil of an electromagnet. It is an ideal device for controlling motors, bells and other electrically noisy equipment. It keeps their power supply totally separate from the logic power supply. This helps to prevent accidents!

51

Fig. 5.15 shows an OR gate controlling a relay through a Darlington Driver. When the output of the OR gate is at logic 0, the motor is stopped. When the output of the OR gate is at logic 1, the motor runs.

The relay on the logic board has a coil which will operate from a $+5$ V supply. As the coil resistance is 56R, it draws a current of 89 mA. The relay must be driven by the Darlington Driver.

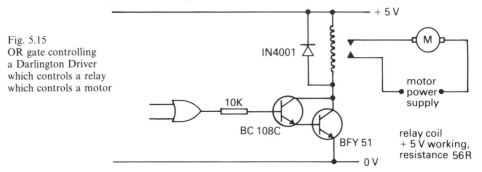

Fig. 5.15
OR gate controlling
a Darlington Driver
which controls a relay
which controls a motor

■ Spikes and Diodes

When an electric current passing though a coil of wire is switched off, the coil generates a high voltage for a brief instant. This **voltage spike** is useful in cars because it makes the spark for the spark plugs. However, it can destroy Darlington Driver transistors if they are not protected by a diode.

Whenever a transistor controls a relay, the relay must have a diode connected across its coil. The diode is connected **reverse biased**, as in Fig. 5.15. Other wire coil devices, such as solenoids, must be treated in the same way if they are controlled by a transistor.

Some relays are manufactured with the diode built in. If you use such a relay, take care that the correct coil connection is taken to the $+5$ V supply and the transistor output. If the connections are reversed, the diode is forward biased and a large current will flow through it when the transistor turns on. This will destroy the diode and the transistor.

■ Symbols

Fig. 5.16 shows symbols used in the Workbooks for the discrete component Darlington Driver and the relay. The symbols are used so that there is no confusion between the permanent connections on the logic board and the ones which you have to make. You should always draw the full circuit diagrams.

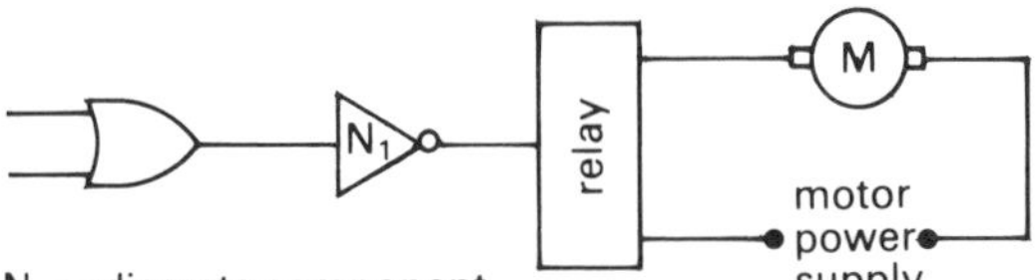

Fig. 5.16
The same circuit as
Fig. 5.15 but as shown
in the Workbooks

N_1 = discrete component
Darlington Driver

■ Relay Controls Relay

It is essential that a relay's contacts are able to handle the load current and voltage. The supplier's catalogue will give these details. If the current and voltage are beyond the contact's capabilities, make the low power relay contacts control the coil of another relay with high power contacts as in Fig. 5.17.

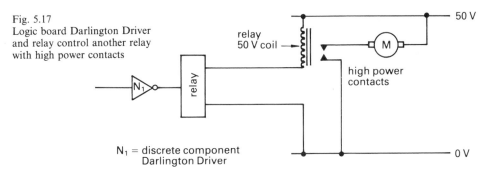

Fig. 5.17
Logic board Darlington Driver
and relay control another relay
with high power contacts

N_1 = discrete component
Darlington Driver

■ Voltage Translation

A Darlington Driver can interface a +5 V logic system and equipment requiring a separate power supply, possibly at a different voltage, e.g. +24 V dc. This is called **voltage translation**. Fig. 5.18 shows how the connections should be made. Note that it is essential to connect the 0 V lines of the 5 V and the 24 V supplies.

This method is recommended if the logic system is to drive a loudspeaker which produces tones.

Fig. 5.18 A Darlington Driver interfacing
a 5 V and a 24 V system

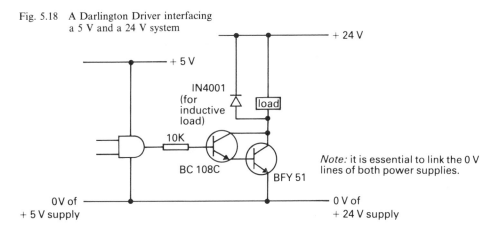

■ The Octal Buffer

If a system needs several Darlington Drivers, it is convenient to use an integrated circuit which contains a number of them. Because the ULN 2803A integrated circuit contains eight Darlington Drivers it is often known as an **octal buffer**. Fig. 5.19a gives the circuit diagram of one of its Darlington Drivers. Fig. 5.19b gives the pin-out of the chip. The chip is explained in greater detail in Chapter 11.

Fig. 5.19   The ULN 2803A octal buffer

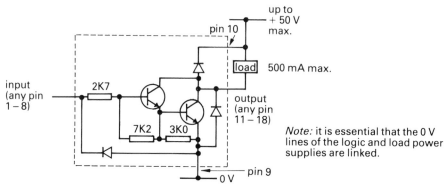

a) One of eight Darlington Driver circuits in the ULN 2803A

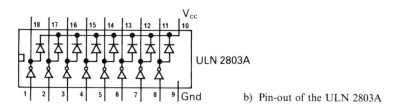

b) Pin-out of the ULN 2803A

On the logic board there are two ULN 2803A chips. One is permanently connected and drives the LEDs which form the 8-bit indicator. The other is not connected in any way and is available for experimental work. For example, it is used in Activity 11 to control the traffic light LEDs on the logic board. It may be used also for advanced work such as interfacing a stepper motor and a computer.

6 The R-S (Reset-Set) Flip-flop

■ If Only It Could Remember!

Fig. 6.1a shows a circuit for a 'person sensor' installed in the doorway shown in Fig. 6.1b.

Fig. 6.1   A sensing situation

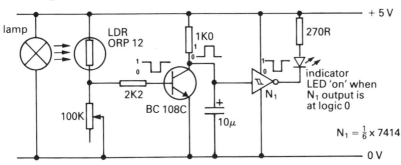

a) A 'person sensing' circuit

Note: ⊓ and ⊓_ show the logic levels in the circuit before, during and after interruption of the light beam.

$N_1 = \frac{1}{6} \times 7414$

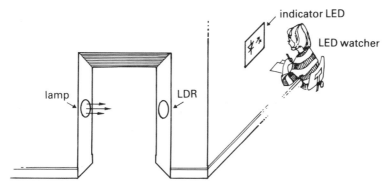

b) Doorway with sensing system installed

As someone walks through the doorway and interrupts the light beam, an indicator LED turns on. The LED stays on for as long as the beam is interrupted. It indicates the event only while it happens. This is satisfactory as long as someone watches the LED continuously. If the LED watcher goes away and then returns, she has no way of knowing if someone has walked through the doorway during her absence. The electronic system would be better if it could remember an interruption of the light beam and indicate it by keeping the LED turned on after the event.

55

■ Memory

Remembering is carried out by a **memory**. There are many digital microelectronic memory circuits. Most of them are able to remember a large amount of information not just one single item. Nevertheless, a memory circuit which can remember just one thing is very useful. It is called a **flip-flop**. Sometimes it is called a **latch** or a **bistable circuit**. It is 'bistable' because its output has two (bi) stable states, logic 0 and logic 1. After being given a momentary input signal, its output moves from one logic level to the other and stays there.

■ Mechanical Memory

A domestic table-light switch (Fig. 6.2) is a mechanical bistable device. If one side of the switch is given a brief push, the switch turns on the light. Further pushes on that side have no effect. The light stays on until the other side of the switch is given a brief push to turn it off. More pushes on that side have no effect.

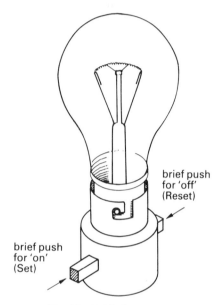

brief push for 'off' (Reset)

brief push for 'on' (Set)

The side of the switch which turns on the light can be called the **Set** side. The side of the switch which turns off the light can be called the **Reset** side.

Fig. 6.2   Table-light switch

■ The Reset-Set (R-S) Flip-flop

Fig. 6.3a shows the symbol for a flip-flop. It has two inputs, Set (S) and Reset (R), and one output, Q.

Imagine that the inputs and the output are at logic 0. If the Set input now moves briefly from logic 0 to logic 1 and back to logic 0, output Q changes from logic 0 to logic 1 and stays there. If the Set input is pulsed again from 0 to 1 and back to 0, output Q is not affected. It stays at logic 1.

If the Reset input is pulsed from logic 0 to logic 1 and back to logic 0,

Fig. 6.3   The flip-flop

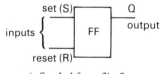

Input signal	State of output Q (start with Q at logic 0)
$S\,^1_0\,$ ⎍	1
$R\,^1_0\,$ ⎍	0

a) Symbol for a flip-flop   b) Truth table for a flip-flop

output Q returns to logic 0 and stays there. If the Reset input is pulsed again, Q is not affected. It stays at logic 0.

This type of flip-flop is known as a **Reset-Set** or **R-S flip-flop**. Its behaviour is summarised in the truth table (Fig. 6.3b).

■ How to Make an R-S Flip-flop (NOR Gates)

Fig. 6.4a shows how two NOR gates may be connected to form an R-S flip-flop. There are two outputs, Q and Q-bar (NOT Q). The two outputs are always at opposite logic levels. In practical applications, either or both of the outputs may be used.

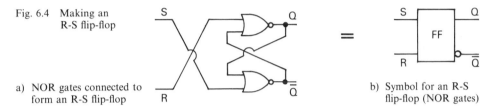

Fig. 6.4   Making an R-S flip-flop

a) NOR gates connected to form an R-S flip-flop

b) Symbol for an R-S flip-flop (NOR gates)

Fig. 6.4b is a symbol for the NOR gate R-S flip-flop circuit. Notice the negation circle on the Q-bar output. It means that this output is always at the opposite logic level to the Q output.

In Fig 6.4a, notice how the output of each NOR gate is connected to the input of the other NOR gate. This type of connection is called **feedback** and it is used in many electronic circuits.

■ A Basic Circuit

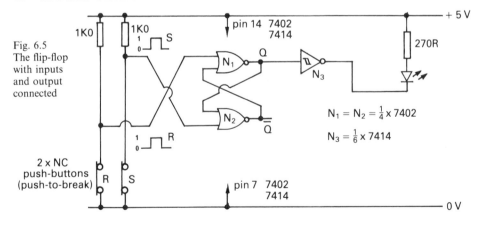

Fig. 6.5 The flip-flop with inputs and output connected

$N_1 = N_2 = \frac{1}{4} \times 7402$

$N_3 = \frac{1}{6} \times 7414$

2 x NC push-buttons (push-to-break)

Fig. 6.5 shows the flip-flop with input and output connections. It is essential that the R and S inputs are held at logic 0 while waiting for something to happen. The use of normally closed **push-to-break** push-button switches does this. You can use the mnemonics: 'NOR at nought'; or 'O in NOR and 0 in logic 0' to help you remember the correct waiting state for this flip-flop.

How It Works

In Fig. 6.5, let Q be at logic 0. Therefore Q-bar is at logic 1. The output of the inverter is at logic 1 and the LED is off.

If the S push-button is momentarily pressed and released, the Set input of the flip-flop moves from logic 0 to 1 and back to 0. This sequence is called a **positive-going pulse**. As a result, Q moves to and stays at logic 1. The output of the inverter moves to logic 0 and the LED turns on.

If the R push-button is momentarily pressed and released, the Reset input of the flip-flop is given a positive-going pulse. Q moves back to and stays at logic 0. The output of the inverter moves to logic 1 and the LED turns off.

The S and R buttons must not be pressed at the same time. This would put both inputs at logic 1 and force both outputs to logic 0. This is known as a **disallowed state** because it breaks the flip-flop rule. It does not harm the chips. The real problem is that there is no way of knowing if Q will be at logic 0 or logic 1 when the buttons are released.

The truth table (Table 6.1) summarises the operation of the flip-flop.

Comment on input	Input		Output		Comment on output
	R	S	Q	$\overline{Q}$	
The 'at rest' state	0	0	Q	$\overline{Q}$	Opposite states 1 and 0 or 0 and 1
Set input pulsed	0	⎍ (0→1→0)	1	0	Input signals give these output states, but if they exist already there is no change in output
Reset input pulsed	⎍ (0→1→0)	0	0	1	
This input state is not allowed	1	1	0	0	

Table 6.1   Truth table for R-S flip-flop (NOR gates)

Practical Application

Fig. 6.6a is an improved version of the person sensor circuit, Fig. 6.1a. A NOR gate R-S flip-flop and two inverters have been added.

Assume that the LED is off. If the light beam is briefly interrupted, a pulse passes through the system to the Set input of the flip-flop. The pulse makes output Q move to logic 1. The output of the final inverter moves to logic 0. The LED turns on. It stays on even if the light beam is repeatedly interrupted. The LED is said to be **latched on**. The LED is turned off by momentary operation of the Reset push-button.

Carefully trace the logic levels at each point in the circuit as the LDR is in the light, then in the dark and then back in the light.

Note that when the flip-flop is waiting for something to happen, i.e. the

Fig. 6.6 The sensing situation improved

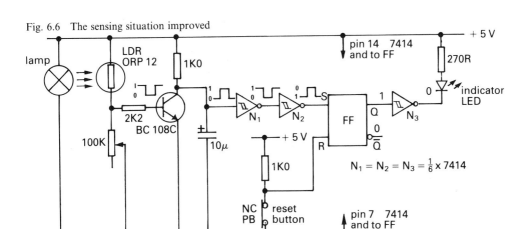

Note: $_0\sqcap^1$ or $_0\sqcup^1$ represent the pulse which passes through the system when the light beam is momentarily interrupted. The resulting logic levels at the outputs of the flip-flop are shown also.

a) Improved person detector circuit

LDR is in the light and the Reset button is not pressed, the R and S inputs are held at logic 0.

If a normally closed push-button switch was not available for the Reset system, a normally open switch could be used. But, an inverter would need to be placed between the switch circuit output and the R input.

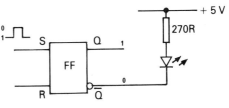

b) Alternative output connections

Fig. 6.6b shows an alternative way for the flip-flop to control the LED. If the Q-bar output is used, the final inverter is not needed. Be sure you understand why.

☐ **Positive-going Pulses**

Fig. 6.7 shows the type of pulse applied to the Set and Reset inputs of a NOR gate flip-flop. It is called a positive-going pulse because it starts at logic 0, rises to logic 1, stays there for a time and then returns to logic 0.

In digital microelectronic systems, the beginning and end of a pulse are very important. These **edges** are used to make other things happen. The beginning of the pulse (Fig. 6.7) is called the **leading edge**. It is a **rising** or **positive-going edge**. The end of the pulse is called the **trailing edge**. It is a **falling** or **negative-going edge**.

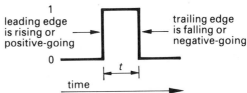

Fig. 6.7 A positive-going pulse

t = duration of the pulse in seconds (also called the pulse width)

59

☐ Know When Things Happen

Manufacturers of digital integrated circuits publish data sheets and books. These give details of their products and how to use them. The information usually includes **timing diagrams** as in Fig. 6.8. A timing diagram shows the relationship between input signals and output changes. It shows when things happen. Without this information, it is impossible to produce successful designs for even simple digital microelectronic systems.

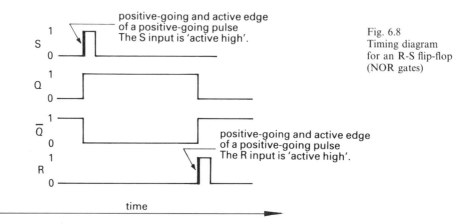

Fig. 6.8
Timing diagram
for an R-S flip-flop
(NOR gates)

You must know when things happen and take it into account in your designs. If you don't, you could easily design, for example, a fire alarm which rings when a fire goes out and not when it starts!

Fig. 6.8 is the timing diagram for a NOR gate R-S flip-flop. Output Q is initially at logic 0 and Q-bar is at logic 1. A brief positive-going pulse is applied to the Set (S) input. The diagram shows that it is the leading, positive-going edge of the pulse which makes the outputs change logic level. The S input is said to be **active-high**. The duration of the S input pulse does not matter as long as it ends before a Reset pulse is applied at the R input.

Fig. 6.8 shows that it is the leading, positive-going edge of the Reset pulse which makes the outputs revert to their original logic levels. The R input is also active-high. The Reset pulse may be of any duration provided it ends before the next Set pulse.

An R-S flip-flop is a **one bit memory** because the Q output can remember one binary digit, a 0 or a 1.

◼ Another Way to Make an R-S Flip-flop

NAND gates may be connected to form an R-S flip-flop, as in Fig. 6.9.

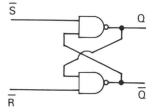

Fig. 6.9   NAND gates connected to form an R-S flip-flop

60

■ A Basic Circuit

The NAND gate circuit as in Fig. 6.10 resembles the NOR circuit, but there is an important difference: the inputs behave in the opposite manner. This is partly why they are labelled R-bar and S-bar. Note that pull-up resistors 'park' the inputs at logic 1. The push-button switches are normally open, **push-to-make**.

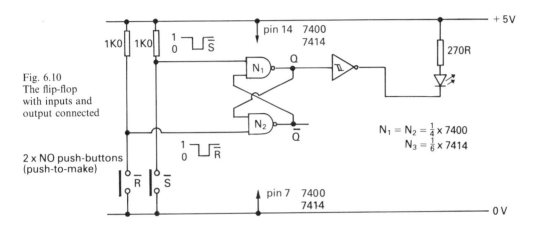

Fig. 6.10
The flip-flop
with inputs and
output connected

$N_1 = N_2 = \frac{1}{4} \times 7400$
$N_3 = \frac{1}{6} \times 7414$

■ How it Works

In Fig. 6.10, let Q be at logic 0. Therefore Q-bar is at logic 1. The output of the inverter is at logic 1. The LED is off.

If the S-bar push button is momentarily pressed and released, the S-bar input moves from logic 1 to 0 and back to 1. This is called a **negative-going pulse**. Q moves to and stays at logic 1. The output of the inverter moves to logic 0 and the LED turns on.

If the R-bar push button is momentarily pressed and released, the R-bar

Comment on input	Input		Output		Comment on output
	$\overline{R}$	$\overline{S}$	Q	$\overline{Q}$	
The 'at rest' state	1	1	Q	$\overline{Q}$	Opposite states 1 and 0 or 0 and 1
Set input pulsed	1	⊓	1	0	Input signals give these output states, but if they exist already there is no change in output
Reset input pulsed	⊔	1	0	1	
This input state is not allowed	0	0	1	1	

Table 6.2   Truth table for R-S flip-flop (NAND gates)

input of the flip-flop is given a negative-going pulse. Q moves to and stays at logic 0. The output of the inverter moves to logic 1 and the LED turns off.

It is important that the S and R buttons are not pressed at the same time. This would put both inputs at logic 0 and force both outputs to logic 1. This is a disallowed state.

The truth table (Table 6.2) summarises the behaviour of this flip-flop.

☐ Negative-going Pulses

Fig. 6.11 shows the type of pulse applied to the Set and Reset inputs of a NAND gate flip-flop. It is called a negative-going pulse because it starts at logic 1, falls to logic 0, stays there for a time, then returns to logic 1.

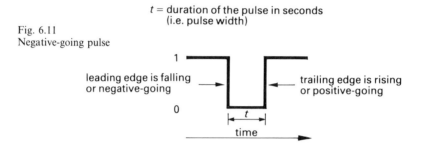

Fig. 6.11
Negative-going pulse

t = duration of the pulse in seconds (i.e. pulse width)

leading edge is falling or negative-going

trailing edge is rising or positive-going

The beginning of the pulse is the leading edge. It is a falling or negative-going edge. The end of the pulse is the trailing edge. It is a rising or positive-going edge.

☐ Know When Things Happen

Fig. 6.12 is the timing diagram for a NAND-based R-S flip-flop. Let Q be at logic 0. Therefore Q-bar is at logic 1. A brief negative-going pulse is applied

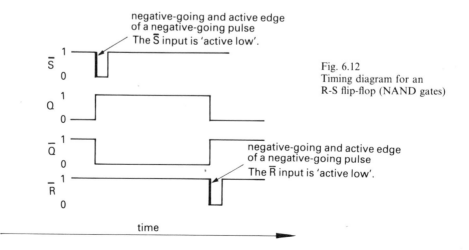

negative-going and active edge of a negative-going pulse
The $\overline{S}$ input is 'active low'.

Fig. 6.12
Timing diagram for an R-S flip-flop (NAND gates)

negative-going and active edge of a negative-going pulse
The $\overline{R}$ input is 'active low'.

time

to the Set input. Fig. 6.12 shows that it is the leading, negative-going edge of the pulse which makes the two outputs change logic level. The input is said to be **active low**. The duration of the Set input pulse does not matter as long as it ends before a Reset pulse is applied.

Fig. 6.12 shows that it is the leading, negative-going edge of the Reset pulse which makes the outputs revert to their original logic levels. This input is also active low. The Reset pulse may be of any duration provided it ends before the next Set pulse.

☐ Active Low and Active High

The terms 'active low' and 'active high' apply to inputs which are operated by pulses. They tell a designer 'when things happen'. If an input on a chip pin-out diagram is labelled with a bar, e.g. R-bar, that input is active low. If there is no bar, the input is active high.

☐ Symbol

Fig. 6.13 shows a symbol for an R-S flip-flop made from NAND gates. Notice the negation circles at the two inputs. This is another convention which says that the inputs receive pulses and are active-low. Inputs without the circles are active-high. The convention is used on chip pin-out diagrams.

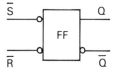

Fig. 6.13   Symbol for an R-S flip-flop (NAND gates)

☐ Practical Application

An R-S flip-flop based on NOR gates requires positive-going input pulses while one based on NAND gates requires negative-going input pulses. Provided these needs are met the two circuits behave identically. Either of them may be used in most practical applications.

Fig. 6.14 is the person-sensing circuit, shown in Fig. 6.6, redrawn to show how an R-S flip-flop based on NAND gates is used to achieve the same result, i.e. momentary interruption of the light beam makes the LED turn on and stay on. Notice that the flip-flop inputs rest at logic 1. Study the circuit by following through the system the pulse generated when the light beam is interrupted momentarily.

Fig. 6.14   The sensing situation

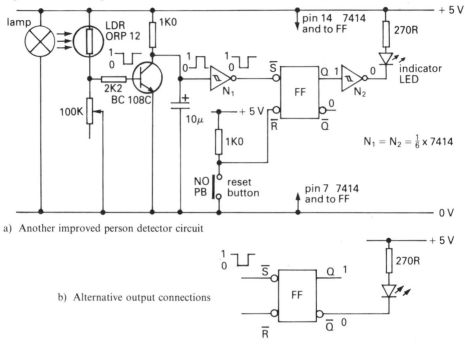

a) Another improved person detector circuit

b) Alternative output connections

$N_1 = N_2 = \frac{1}{6} \times 7414$

□   Don't Take Chances

When the circuits in Fig. 6.6 and Fig. 6.14 are first switched on, output Q
needs to be at logic 0. What actually happens at power-up with any type of
flip-flop is a matter of chance. An output can settle at either logic level. In
some systems this may not matter. Operation of a reset button will sort things
out if necessary. But if the flip-flop controls, say, a burglar alarm bell, it is
essential that it automatically resets at power-up, i.e. always starts with
output Q at logic 0.

Power-on reset can be guaranteed if a pull-up resistor is connected to
output Q-bar as in Fig. 6.15. You may have to experiment with different
value resistors before a circuit functions reliably. This is because the power-

Fig. 6.15
How to guarantee
Q at logic 0 at
power-up

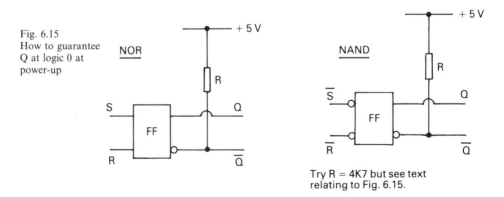

Try R = 4K7 but see text
relating to Fig. 6.15.

64

up behaviour depends on the loads already connected to its Q and Q-bar outputs. Start with 4K7 but, if necessary, increase up to 10K or reduce down to 1K0. The pull-up resistor is in addition to any other load which may be connected to the outputs.

■ Another Contact Debouncing Circuit

In Chapter 5 a contact debouncing circuit was described. It was made from a resistor, a capacitor and a Schmitt inverter. It is a useful circuit but cannot debounce a switch which is being operated many times in very rapid succession.

An R-S flip-flop is an excellent circuit for debouncing contacts. It has no speed limitation. It will debounce a switch which is being operated at the maximum repetition rate its mechanism allows. The switch must be of the single-pole-double-throw (SPDT) type. Often, these switches are called changeover switches. Microswitches, relays, slide switches and reed switches can be obtained in this form.

SPDT switches have three contacts. One of them is a 'common' (COM) contact. When the switch is not operated, the common contact touches a normally closed (NC) contact. When the switch is operated the common contact touches a normally open (NO) contact.

The R-S flip-flop used to debounce an SPDT switch must be made from NAND gates as in Fig. 6.16. This is because the common contact does not touch either of the other contacts while the switch mechanism is moving. This makes both flip-flop inputs go to logic 1. This is allowable only with a NAND gate flip-flop (see Table 6.2 and Table 6.1).

Fig. 6.16   Debouncing circuit for an SPDT switch (a changeover switch)

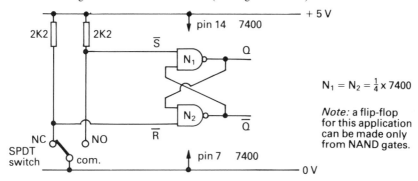

$N_1 = N_2 = \frac{1}{4} \times 7400$

Note: a flip-flop for this application can be made only from NAND gates.

Study the debouncing circuit (Fig. 6.16) and, with the help of Table 6.2 and Fig. 6.12, be sure to understand how and why the circuit works. There is an SPDT slide switch on the logic board which can be used to demonstrate this circuit.

7 The J-K Flip-flop

■ More Light Switches

Fig. 7.1 shows two types of switch widely used to turn lights on and off. In Fig. 7.1a, if the button is pushed once, the light turns on. If the button is pushed again, the light turns off. If the button is pushed a third time, the light turns on again...and so on. Pull switches, as in Fig. 7.1b, work in a similar manner. Pull the cord once, the light turns on. Pull the cord again, the light turns off...and so on.

Fig. 7.1 Lamps and switches

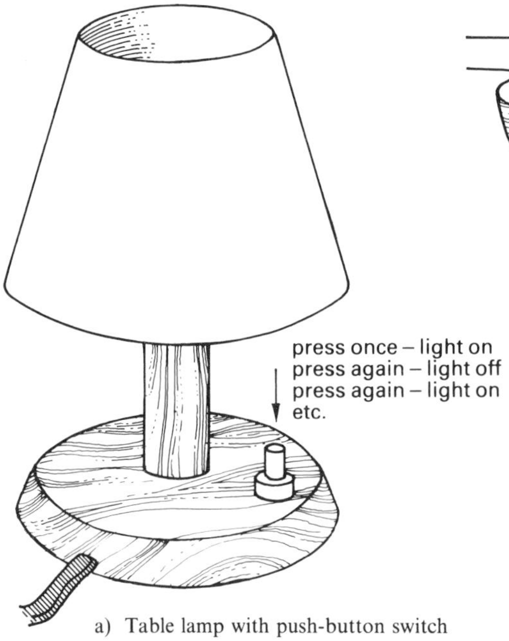

press once – light on
press again – light off
press again – light on
etc.

pull once – light on
pull again – light off
pull again – light on
etc.

a) Table lamp with push-button switch 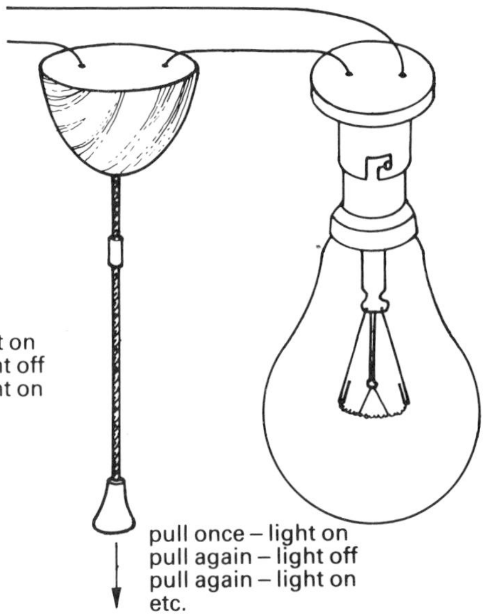   b) Bathroom lamp with pull switch

■ Single Input Flip-flop

The important feature of both of the switches (Fig. 7.1) is that each has only one input. Each time the input is operated, the output changes state and stays there until the input is operated again.

There is an important digital microelectronic circuit which behaves in a similar way. It is another flip-flop. Unlike the R-S flip-flop, it has only one input, as in Fig. 7.2a. This is known as the **clock (CLK) input**.

The truth table (Fig. 7.2b) shows that the output changes logic level every time the CLK input receives a pulse. An output which behaves like this is said to be **toggling**. This behaviour is summarised in the abbreviated truth table, Fig. 7.2c.

Fig. 7.2   Single input flip-flop

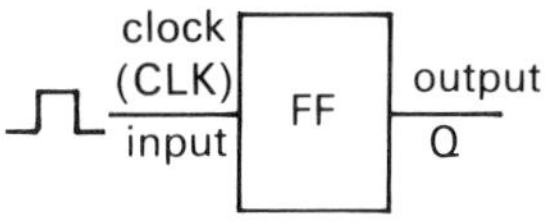

a) Symbol for a single input flip-flop (one output)

	Input	Output
	CLK	Q (initially at logic 0)
Pulse 1	⎍	1
Pulse 2	⎍	0
Pulse 3	⎍	1
Pulse 4	⎍	0
etc.	etc.	etc.

b) Truth table showing output state after successive clock pulses

Input	Output
CLK	Q
⎍	toggle

c) Abbreviated truth table

Two Outputs

Like the R-S flip-flop, a practical single input flip-flop has two outputs, Q and Q-bar as in Fig. 7.3a. These outputs are always at opposite logic levels. Either or both of the outputs may be used. The truth table (Fig. 7.3b) shows how the outputs change logic level with successive clock pulses. Fig. 7.3c gives the Fig.7.3b information in abbreviated form.

Fig. 7.3   Single input flip-flop

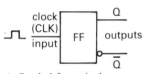

a) Symbol for a single input flip-flop (two outputs)

	Input	Outputs	
	CLK	Q (initially Q = logic 0 $\overline{Q}$ = logic 1)	$\overline{Q}$
Pulse 1	⎍	1	0
Pulse 2	⎍	0	1
Pulse 3	⎍	1	0
Pulse 4	⎍	0	1
etc.	etc.	etc.	etc.

b) Truth table showing output state after successive clock pulses

Input	Outputs	
CLK	Q	$\overline{Q}$
⎍	toggle	

c) Abbreviated truth table

The J-K Flip-flop

A single input flip-flop is not available as a digital integrated circuit. However, there are flip-flop integrated circuits which have several inputs. Many of these circuits may be connected so that they behave like a single input flip-flop. One of them is a **J-K flip-flop with clear** as in Fig. 7.4a. In the standard TTL range its code number is 7473. It contains two independent flip-flops as in Fig. 7.4b.

Fig. 7.4
The J-K flip-flop

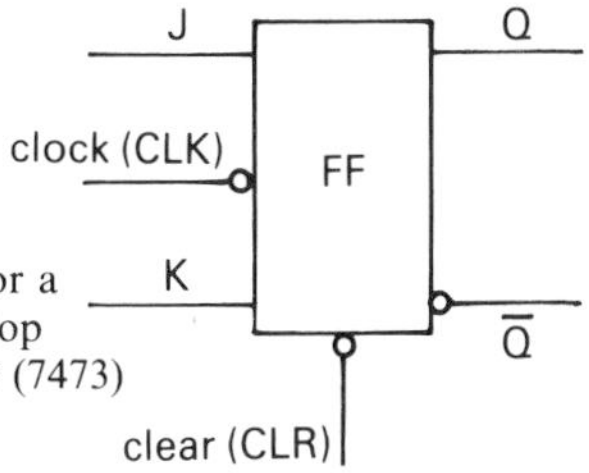

a) Symbol for a J-K flip-flop with clear (7473)

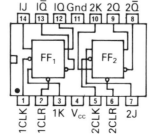

b) Pin-out of 7473 dual J-K negative edge-triggered flip-flop

67

■ Making Connections

Each flip-flop in the 7473 chip has four inputs, **CLK (clock)**, **CLR (clear)**, and **J** and **K**. Fig. 7.5 shows how this J-K flip-flop is connected to form a single input flip-flop. As the CLR, J and K inputs are not required, they are held at logic 1 by connection to the 5 V supply. A push-button with a debouncing circuit is connected to the CLK input.

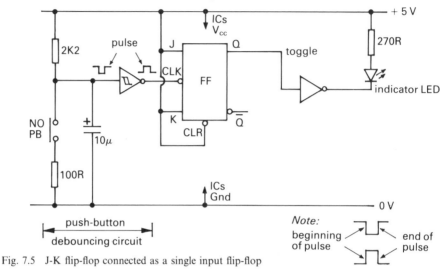

Fig. 7.5   J-K flip-flop connected as a single input flip-flop

Each time the push-button is pressed and released, a clock pulse is supplied to the flip-flop and its outputs, Q and Q-bar, change logic level. In Fig. 7.5, the logic level of Q is displayed by an indicator LED. When Q is at logic 1, the indicator is on. When Q is at logic 0, the indicator is off.

□ Know When Things Happen

Fig. 7.5 shows a single pulse as it passes through the circuit from the push-button to the clock input of the flip-flop. The beginning of the pulse marks the instant when the button is pressed. The end of the pulse marks the instant when the button is released. A circuit designer must know which part of a clock pulse makes the flip-flop outputs change logic level. The designer gets this information from a timing diagram.

The timing diagram (Fig. 7.6) shows that it is the negative-going edge of a

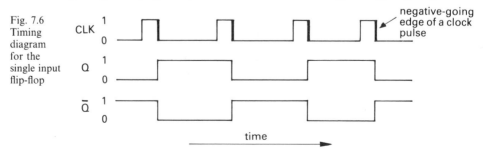

Fig. 7.6 Timing diagram for the single input flip-flop

68

clock pulse which makes the outputs change logic level. Therefore, it is at the end of the positive-going clock pulse in Fig. 7.5 that the flip-flop outputs change state. This corresponds to the moment when the push-button is released.

The same conclusion could have been reached from information in Fig. 7.4a. It shows the clock input of the 7473 flip-flop symbol marked with a negation circle. This means that the input is active low. Therefore it is the negative-going edge of a clock pulse which makes the outputs change logic level.

☐ Changing Things Round

The designer can arrange for the flip-flop outputs to **toggle** when the push-button is first pressed. To make this happen, another inverter is added to the circuit, as in Fig. 7.7.

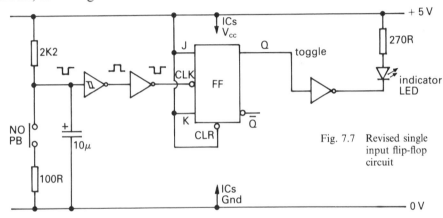

Fig. 7.7   Revised single input flip-flop circuit

Fig. 7.7 shows a single pulse as it passes through the circuit from the push-button to the clock input of the flip-flop. At the clock input the pulse is negative-going. It is the leading, negative-going edge of the pulse which makes the outputs toggle. This corresponds to the moment when the push-button is pressed.

The performance of the circuit in Fig. 7.7 is described by a revised timing diagram as in Fig. 7.8. It shows the relationship between the leading edge of the negative-going clock pulses and the changes of output logic level.

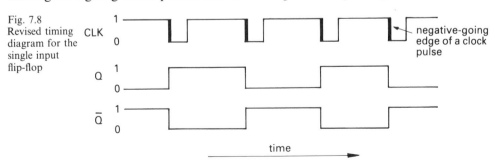

Fig. 7.8 Revised timing diagram for the single input flip-flop

□ No 'Parking Problem'

Unlike the R-S flip-flops, the clock input of the 7473 flip-flop may be 'parked' at either logic level. It all depends on whether the outputs are to toggle at the beginning or the end of an event. They may be toggled by the trailing edge of a positive-going pulse as in Fig. 7.6, or by the leading edge of a negative-going pulse as in Fig. 7.8. In both cases, the active edges are negative-going.

■ A Frequency Divider

Fig. 7.9 is part of the Fig. 7.6 timing diagram. Four clock pulses are shown. They produce two complete pulses at the Q output. Thus, a flip-flop is a circuit which can **divide an input by two**. It is a **frequency divider**. For example, if the clock input was being pulsed 880 times a second, a frequency of 880 Hz, the Q output would produce 440 pulses a second, a frequency of 440 Hz. In musical terms, these frequencies are an **octave** apart. 440 Hz is the frequency of the note A above middle C. 800 Hz is the frequency of the note A an octave higher. The flip-flop enables the lower frequency to be generated from the higher frequency.

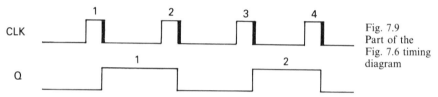

Fig. 7.9
Part of the
Fig. 7.6 timing
diagram

■ Cascading Flip-flops

Flip-flops may be cascaded, i.e. the output of one flip-flop may be connected to the clock input of another flip-flop as in Fig. 7.10.

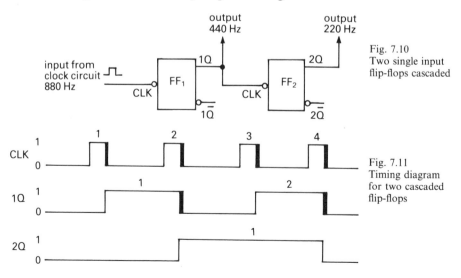

Fig. 7.10
Two single input
flip-flops cascaded

Fig. 7.11
Timing diagram
for two cascaded
flip-flops

Fig. 7.11 is the timing diagram for two cascaded flip-flops. For every four pulses at the clock input, output 1Q produces two pulses and output 2Q produces one pulse. Thus, if the clock frequency was 880 Hz, the frequency at 1Q would be 440 Hz and the frequency at 2Q would be 220 Hz. In musical terms, the frequencies decrease in **octave steps**. If more flip-flops are cascaded, more octave intervals are obtained.

☐ Make Music

An **automatic clock circuit** can generate a continuous stream of pulses which can be applied to the CLK input of a flip-flop. These circuits are studied in Chapter 8. Twelve of them could be constructed to give each of the frequencies in the octave-8 line of Table 7.1. If each clock drives its own chain of eight cascaded flip-flops, all of the frequencies of the **twelve-note equally tempered musical scale** are generated as in Table 7.1. Such a system can form the tone generation section of a musical instrument such as an electronic organ or an electronic piano.

Each note in the equally tempered scale is, musically speaking, a semitone higher or lower than its immediate neighbours. If the frequency of a note is known, the frequencies of its neighbours are found by multiplying or dividing

Octave number	Note					
	C	C#	D	D#	E	F
0	16.352	17.324	18.354	19.445	20.602	21.827
1	32.703	34.648	36.708	38.891	41.203	43.654
2	65.406	69.296	73.416	77.782	82.407	87.307
3	130.81	138.59	146.83	155.56	164.81	174.61
4	261.63	277.18	293.66	311.13	329.63	349.23
5	523.25	554.37	587.33	622.25	659.26	698.46
6	1046.5	1108.7	1174.7	1244.5	1318.5	1396.9
7	2093.0	2217.5	2349.3	2489.0	2637.0	2793.8
8	4186.0	4434.9	4698.6	4978.0	5274.0	5587.7

Octave number	Note					
	F#	G	G#	A	A#	B
0	23.125	24.500	25.957	27.500	29.135	30.868
1	46.249	48.999	51.913	55.000	58.270	61.735
2	92.499	97.999	103.83	110.00	116.54	123.47
3	185.00	196.00	207.65	220.00	233.08	246.94
4	369.99	392.00	415.30	440.00	466.16	493.88
5	739.99	783.99	830.61	880.00	932.33	987.77
6	1480.0	1568.0	1661.2	1760.0	1864.7	1975.5
7	2960.0	3136.0	3322.4	3520.0	3729.3	3851.1
8	5919.9	6271.9	6644.9	7040.0	7458.6	7902.1

Table 7.1   Frequencies of the twelve-note equally tempered musical scale

the known frequency by the twelfth root of 2, $\sqrt[12]{2}$, i.e. 1.059 463 1. For example, as the frequency of A is 440 Hz, the frequency of the note a semitone higher, A♮, is 440 Hz × 1.059 463 1 = 466.16 Hz. The frequency of the note a semitone lower, G♮, is 440 Hz/1.059 463 1 = 415.30 Hz. You could check some of the numbers in Table 7.1 with your calculator.

■ A Counter

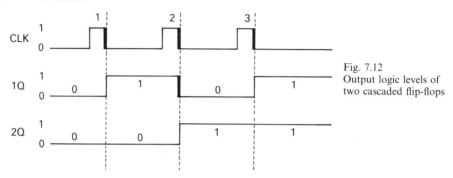

Fig. 7.12
Output logic levels of two cascaded flip-flops

Fig. 7.12 is another look at the timing diagram for two cascaded flip-flops in Fig. 7.10. It highlights the output logic levels at the end of each of three successive clock pulses. Initially both outputs are at logic 0. Therefore, from Fig. 7.12:

$$\text{Start, } 2Q = \text{logic 0, } 1Q = \text{logic 0}$$
$$\text{After pulse 1, } 2Q = \text{logic 0, } 1Q = \text{logic 1}$$
$$\text{After pulse 2, } 2Q = \text{logic 1, } 1Q = \text{logic 0}$$
$$\text{After pulse 3, } 2Q = \text{logic 1, } 1Q = \text{logic 1}$$

This information is summarised in Table 7.2.

Each pair of logic levels for outputs 1Q and 2Q is a 2-bit binary number. The number is equal to the total number of clock pulses up to that point, as in Table 7.3. The cascaded flip-flops form a **counter** which counts the clock pulses.

Number of CLK pulse	Outputs 2Q	1Q
0	0	0
1	0	1
2	1	0
3	1	1

Table 7.2 Summary of output logic levels

Binary output 2Q twos 2^1	1Q ones 2^0	Decimal equivalent
0	0	0
0	1	1
1	0	2
1	1	3

Table 7.3 Flip-flop output in a binary count

The maximum binary count for two cascaded flip-flops is 11. Binary 11 is the equivalent of decimal 3. The maximum count is extended if more flip-flops are cascaded. Four flip-flops can output a 4-bit binary number, a nibble.

Its maximum value is 1111. This is the equivalent of decimal 15. Eight flip-flops can output an 8-bit binary number, a byte. Its maximum value is 1111 1111. This is the equivalent of decimal 255.

A binary count can be displayed if an LED indicator circuit is connected to each flip-flop output. When connecting the LEDs, remember that the first flip-flop in a chain gives the least significant bit, LSB, of the count. The last flip-flop gives the most significant bit, MSB. Therefore, the LED which displays the LSB should be placed on the extreme right and the MSB LED must be on the extreme left.

A binary read-out from a flip-flop counting circuit is not readily understood. Additional circuits and devices may be connected to the flip-flops to give a decimal display of the count.

Counters and displays are studied in depth in Chapters 9 and 10.

□ Comment on Counters

The single input flip-flop is the basic building-block of many digital microelectronic counters.

A counter made from cascaded flip-flops is called a **ripple** or **asynchronous counter**. This is because it takes a fraction of a second for the effect of a pulse at the clock input of the first flip-flop to ripple through the chain to the last flip-flop. In consequence, the outputs of the flip-flops change state one after the other and not all at the same time. In some high speed circuits, the ripple effect can cause serious problems. In this case the designer would use a **synchronous counter**. This is a counter whose outputs change logic level together.

■ Manual Reset

At **power-up**, a J-K flip-flop behaves in a manner similar to an R-S flip-flop. The logic levels of the outputs, while always opposite, are a matter of chance. This causes no problems if the flip-flop is being used as a frequency divider. But, if the flip-flop is being used as a counter, it is essential that counting begins from zero. Therefore the flip-flop must be capable of being **reset** so that Q is at logic 0. The flip-flop's CLR (clear) input is used to achieve this as in Fig. 7.13.

The symbol for the 7473 J-K flip-flop shows the CLR input has a negation circle. It means that this input is active low. If the CLR input is taken momentarily from logic 1 to logic 0 the flip-flop resets.

Fig. 7.13 shows a manually operated reset circuit. A pull-up resistor holds the CLR input at logic 1. This is the 'parking' level for normal functioning of the flip-flop. If the normally open push-button is pressed, the CLR input is pulled down to logic 0 and the flip-flop resets. The push-button circuit does not need to be debounced. It may be connected to other flip-flops in the

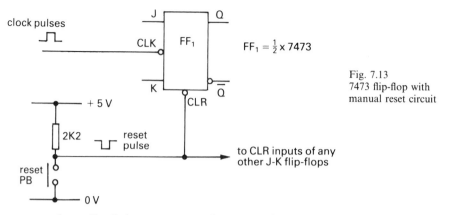

Fig. 7.13
7473 flip-flop with
manual reset circuit

system so that all of them reset at the same time. For as long as the push-button is pressed and the CLR input is at logic 0, the CLK, J and K inputs can have no effect on the outputs. They stay reset.

■ Automatic Power-on Reset

A flip-flop can be made to reset automatically at power-up. This is achieved by replacing the push-button of Fig. 7.13 with a capacitor, as in Fig. 7.14a. It takes time for the capacitor to charge through the pull-up resistor at power-up. Therefore, point A is held at logic 0 for a few milliseconds after power-up. This is sufficient to reset the flip-flop.

Fig. 7.14   Power-on reset circuits

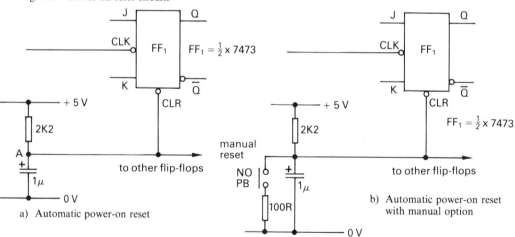

a) Automatic power-on reset

b) Automatic power-on reset
with manual option

■ Manual and Automatic Reset

Often it is necessary to reset a flip-flop after power-up. This is possible if a push-button in series with a low value resistor is added to the automatic power-on reset circuit as in Fig. 7.14b. The circuit is now identical to part of the contact debouncing circuit.

74

☐ Watch the Timing

At power-up, a system may generate signals which can affect flip-flops. For example, a debouncing circuit which uses a resistor and a capacitor, as in Fig. 7.5, will generate a pulse at power-up. Therefore, it is essential that a power-on reset signal lasts longer than these other signals so that the system has time to settle down.

The duration of the reset signal is governed by the values of the pull-up resistor and the capacitor. The **time constant** of these components in series, as in Fig. 7.14a, gives an indication of the duration of the reset signal. The time constant is given by T in the equation:

$$T = C \times R$$

where T is in seconds, C is in farads and R is in ohms.

The time constant of the reset circuit needs to be at least three times that of any other resistor-capacitor (R-C) circuit which can produce a pulse which can affect a flip-flop at power-up. For TTL integrated circuits, a pull-up resistor of between 1K0 and 4K7 is satisfactory. The value of the capacitor can vary widely to suit the system.

☐ The J-K Flip-flop in Detail

Table 7.4 gives the complete function table for the 7473 dual J-K negative edge-triggered flip-flop. Referring to Table 7.4:

Line 1   summarises the reset function described above.

Line 2   says that if CLR = logic 1 and the J and K inputs = logic 0, a CLK pulse has no effect on the outputs. They remain as they are at 0 and 1 or 1 and 0. This is useful if it is necessary to stop clock pulses affecting the flip-flop outputs.

	Inputs				Outputs	
	CLEAR	CLOCK	J	K	Q	$\overline{Q}$
Line 1	0	X	X	X	0	1
Line 2	1	⎍	0	0	Q	$\overline{Q}$
Line 3	1	⎍	1	0	1	0
Line 4	1	⎍	0	1	0	1
Line 5	1	⎍	1	1	Toggle	

Note: X = either logic level

Table 7.4   Complete function table for the 7473 dual J-K negative edge-triggered flip-flop

Line 3   says that if CLR and J = logic 1 and K = logic 0, the negative-going edge of the next clock pulse puts Q at logic 1 and Q-bar at logic 0. If they are already at these levels they are unchanged. This function is useful if it is necessary to preset the outputs. Also, it allows an output change to be made ready at the inputs but not be actioned until the clock, in effect, says 'Go'.

Line 4   says that if CLR and K = logic 1 and J = logic 0, the negative-going edge of the next clock pulse puts Q at logic 0 and Q-bar at logic 1. If they are already at these levels they are unchanged. Again, this is useful if it is necessary to preset the outputs. Also it allows an output change to be made ready at the inputs but not be actioned until the clock says 'Go'.

Line 5   summarises the conditions for toggling of the outputs as described above.

□ A Practical Application

In a breakfast cereal factory, packets of cornflakes move along a conveyor belt. At a certain point, the packets pass through a beam of light which shines on a light-dependent resistor. When three packets have passed through the light beam, an indicator LED turns on. The LED turns off when the first packet in the second batch of three has passed through the light beam. The LED turns on again when the third packet of the second batch has passed through the beam...and so on.

Fig. 7.15 shows the indicating system used in the factory. It combines many of the logic functions and circuits studied so far.

Spend a while studying Fig. 7.15 and the 'How it works' explanation. It will help you revise earlier work and help you understand how each part of the system is designed to match with its neighbour. You may need to go over it slowly several times.

□ How It Works

1 Counting at the right moment
Fig. 7.15a shows the sensing system and a single pulse as it passes through the circuit. The beginning of the pulse marks the moment when a packet starts to interrupt the light beam. The end of the pulse marks the moment when the packet has just passed through the light beam. The pulses from the sensing circuit clock a counting circuit as in Fig. 7.15b. The flip-flops increment on the negative-going edge of a pulse. The system requires the flip-flops to alter their outputs when a packet finishes passing through the light beam. Therefore, the sensing circuit is designed to output a positive-going pulse. This has the important negative-going edge at its end as in Fig. 7.15a. So, counting happens at the right moment.

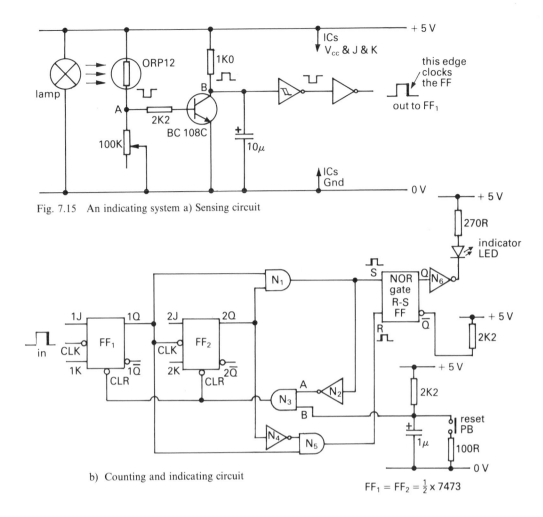

Fig. 7.15   An indicating system a) Sensing circuit

b) Counting and indicating circuit

$$FF_1 = FF_2 = \tfrac{1}{2} \times 7473$$

2   Turning on the LED

In Fig. 7.15b, two cascaded flip-flops form a counter. Their outputs increment in binary from 00 to 11 (decimal 0 to 3) as each packet passes out of the light beam. FF_1 gives the LSB of the count while FF_2 gives the MSB. After the third packet, the outputs of both flip-flops, 2Q and 1Q, are at logic 1. This makes the output of the AND gate, N_1, go from logic 0 to logic 1. This positive-going change triggers the NOR gate R-S flip-flop. Its Q output moves to logic 1. This causes inverter N_6 to turn on the indicator LED.

The count for the first three packets runs from 00 to 01 to 10 to 11. The count for the second three packets must also begin from 00. Therefore, once the first count reaches 11, the J-K flip-flops must immediately reset to 00 in readiness for the first of the next three packets. Let's see how this is done.

3   Resetting the flip-flops

A J-K flip-flop counts when its CLR input is held at logic 1. It resets if the CLR input is momentarily pulled down to logic 0. The output of AND gate

N_3 is normally at logic 1. But, when the output of N_1 is at logic 1, the output of inverter N_2 moves to logic 0. This makes the output of N_3 move to logic 0 and the J-K flip-flops reset. This changes the output of N_1 to logic 0. The output of N_2 moves to logic 1. This makes the output of N_3 return to logic 1 so that the second batch of three packets may be counted.

Now we have to turn off the indicator LED.

4 Turning off the LED

When the first packet of the second batch has passed through the light beam, the output from the J-K flip-flops is binary 01. This means that output 1Q is at logic 1 while output 2Q is at logic 0. This makes the output of N_4 move to logic 1. Thus both of the inputs of AND gate N_5 are at logic 1. Therefore the output of N_5 moves from logic 0 to logic 1. This positive-going change resets the R-S flip-flop causing its Q output to return to logic 0. Consequently N_6 turns off the indicator LED.

The circuit could be simplified slightly. Inverter N_6 could be omitted and the LED connected directly to the Q-bar output of the R-S flip-flop. The complete circuit would function as before.

Input B of N_3 is connected to an automatic power-on reset circuit. This ensures that the count of the first batch of packets begins at 00. Thus, a momentary logic 0 at either input A OR input B of AND gate N_3 brings its output to logic 0 to reset the J-K flip-flops. It may seem odd that an AND gate is acting as an OR gate but this is the case and is explained below.

☐ Another Way of Looking at an AND Gate

Table 7.5 shows a truth table for a 2-input AND gate. From the truth table we usually read that the output is at logic 1 only when all the inputs are at logic 1. This reading is according to the terms of **positive logic**.

However, the truth table can be read another way. It says that the output is at logic 0 if one or more of the inputs is at logic 0. This is a reading according to the terms of **negative logic**. It describes a negative logic OR gate.

Inputs		Output
B	A	Q
0	0	0
0	1	0
1	0	0
1	1	1

Table 7.5   A truth table

In Fig. 7.15b, logic gate N_3 is being used as a negative logic OR gate.

☐ Negative Logic

In digital microelectronics, circuit diagrams and texts are worked out in positive logic. However, design problems often have odd corners which cannot be solved by positive logic, for example, the resetting of the J-K flip-flops in Fig. 7.15b. If you find yourself completely stuck on some little detail, remember that positive logic is only 'half the story'. The insoluble problem will probably yield to the opposite approach of negative logic.

Similarly, the operation of a circuit designed by another person may be hard to understand because one or two gates do not 'make sense'. Here again, interpretation according to negative logic may be helpful.

The four basic positive logic functions, AND, OR, NAND and NOR, give the opposite functions in negative logic as in Table 7.6 . You could write out the four truth tables and then read them from a positive logic and then a negative logic point of view in order to test this.

Gate function		
Positive logic	**Negative logic**	
AND	becomes	OR
OR	becomes	AND
NAND	becomes	NOR
NOR	becomes	NAND

Table 7.6   Positive and negative logic functions compared

8 Clocks

■ Introduction

If you observe the seconds hand of a mechanical watch or a large clock, you will see that it does not rotate smoothly. It moves in a series of steps or pulses.

Notice two things about the movement of the seconds hand:

1. the time interval between the start of one step and the start of the next is always the same. For a watch, the interval might be 0.2 seconds; for a clock, 1 second.

2. the number of steps required to rotate the hand once in a minute is always the same. For the watch this number is 300 and, for the clock, 60.

The time-keeping accuracy of the watch or clock depends on the accuracy of the movement pulses. The interval between pulses must be constant as must the number of pulses per minute. Over the centuries, skilled clockmakers have produced mechanisms of amazing accuracy, as in Fig. 8.1.

Fig. 8.1 A clock mechanism

Many electronic systems need a constant supply of pulses. The pulses must be accurate in their spacing and accurate in their number per second. They may be used for time keeping, as in a digital watch or clock. They may be used to ensure that a computer operates in an orderly 'one thing at a time'

80

manner. They may be used to make musical tones in, say, an electronic organ or a synthesiser.

In electronics, a system which generates a stream of pulses has various names: **oscillator**, **astable multivibrator**, **clock**, **clock pulse generator**. Most people involved in digital microelectronics use the term **clock**. The pulses produced by a clock are an endless series of changes of logic level from 0 to 1 and back to 0 and so on, as in Fig. 8.2a.

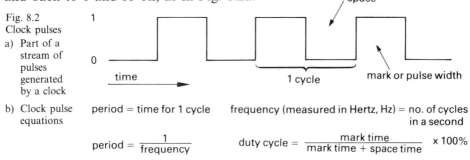

Fig. 8.2
Clock pulses
a) Part of a stream of pulses generated by a clock

b) Clock pulse equations

period = time for 1 cycle   frequency (measured in Hertz, Hz) = no. of cycles in a second

$$\text{period} = \frac{1}{\text{frequency}} \qquad \text{duty cycle} = \frac{\text{mark time}}{\text{mark time} + \text{space time}} \times 100\%$$

■ Pulse Details

From Fig. 8.2a and Fig. 8.2b notice the following:

1 one complete sequence of logic level changes by a clock is called a **cycle**. The time taken for one cycle is the clock **period**. It is measured in seconds. A very 'slow' clock might have a period of many hundreds of seconds. A very 'fast' clock might have a period of less than a millionth of a second.

2 the number of cycles occuring in one second is the clock **frequency**. It is measured in **hertz (Hz)**. Note that

clock period (s) = 1/frequency (Hz)

A slow clock may have a frequency of a few hertz. A very fast clock may have a frequency measured in kilohertz (kHz) or even megahertz (MHz).

3 the time for which the clock output is at logic 1 is called the **mark**. It is known also as the **pulse width**.

4 the time for which the clock output is at logic 0 is called the **space**.

The ratio of the mark time to the total of the the mark and space times is called the **duty cycle** of the clock. It is usually given as a percentage as:

$$\text{duty cycle} = \frac{\text{mark time}}{\text{mark time} + \text{space time}} \times 100\%$$

The mark and space times need not be equal. If they are, the duty cycle is 50%.

The mark and space are the electronic equivalent of the 'tick' and 'tock' of a mechanical clock. Ideally, a mechanical clock has a steady tick-tock-tick-tock sound: a duty cycle of 50%. If the clock is not adjusted correctly, the sound is tick-tock – – – – tick-tock – – – – : a duty cycle other than 50%.

81

☐ Generate a Pulse Stream with a Pendulum

Clock pulses can be generated in various ways. One way involves the adaptation of a mechanical clock (Fig. 8.3). A small permanent magnet is attached to its pendulum. When the pendulum is on the right, the reed switch is closed. As the pendulum swings to the left, the reed switch opens. It stays open until the pendulum swings to the right again, as in Fig. 8.3a.

Fig. 8.3   Clock pulses generated mechanically

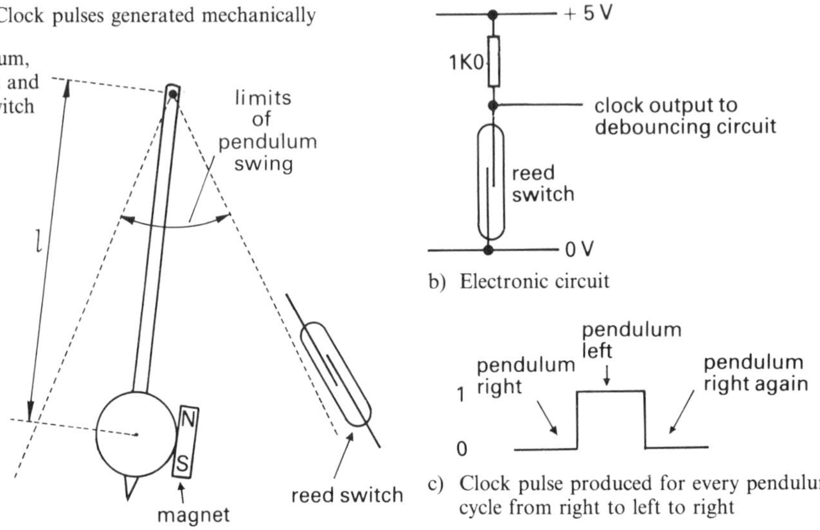

a) Pendulum, magnet and reed switch

b) Electronic circuit

c) Clock pulse produced for every pendulum cycle from right to left to right

The electronic circuit is simple and familiar. The reed switch is connected to a pull-up resistor and a debouncing circuit, as in Fig. 8.3b. Each pendulum cycle, from right to left to right, makes the clock circuit generate a pulse, as in Fig. 8.3c. The frequency of the clock is altered a little by varying the length l of the pendulum.

If the reed switch is repositioned at the centre of the pendulum's swing, the output of the circuit would be twice the frequency of the pendulum.

The reed switch and magnet could be replaced by a light beam shining on a light-dependent resistor. They would be positioned so that the pendulum interrupts the light beam with each swing.

A pulse generation system which depends on the movement of a pendulum is not very convenient and certainly not portable. It can give only low frequencies.

☐ Generate a Pulse Stream with a Disc

A disc can be used to produce clock pulses over a wide range of frequencies. The disc is rotated by an electric motor running at a constant speed. The disc is pierced by a hole near its circumference. A light source and a light sensor are mounted either side of the disc, in line with each other and the hole. Once in every revolution, light passes through the hole to the sensor, as in Fig. 8.4a.

An LDR cannot be used as the light sensor. It cannot respond quickly

Fig. 8.4   Rotating disc clock pulse generator

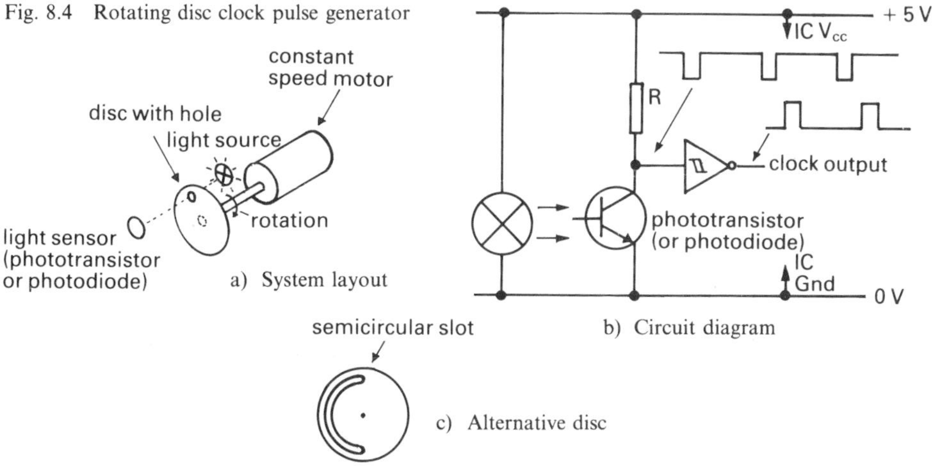

a) System layout

b) Circuit diagram

c) Alternative disc

enough to the brief exposure to light which results when the disc rotates rapidly. A **phototransistor** or a **photodiode** must be used. These devices conduct when light shines on them. They are easy to use. The basic circuit is given in Fig. 8.4b. More details can be obtained from a manufacturer's or supplier's catalogue or data sheets.

As the disc rotates, the electronic circuit produces a succession of pulses. The mark and the space are not equal (Fig. 8.4b). If necessary, they may be made equal in one of two ways:

1   either, the disc with a hole can be replaced by a disc with a semicircular slot, as in Fig. 8.4c, or

2   the output from the circuit (Fig. 8.4b) can toggle a J-K flip-flop.

The flip-flop output gives clock pulses with an equal mark and space, i.e. a 50% duty cycle. However, the frequency is halved. The frequency may be restored to its original value in two ways:

1   either, double the speed of the electric motor, or

2   put a second hole in the disc exactly opposite the first.

Even though the motor runs at one fixed speed, many different frequencies may be generated if discs are used which have appropriate numbers of equally spaced holes. The frequency generated is given by:

frequency (Hz) = speed of disc (revs per second) × no. of holes

Frequency generation by rotating discs was extensively developed and used by the Hammond organ company. For many years they used 'tone wheels' to generate the pitches for the notes of their electronic organs.

An alternative to the rotating disc, light source and sensor is a rotating toothed wheel. The wheel is like a gear wheel and made of ferrous metal. A magnetic sensor is supported close to the teeth on the wheel. As each tooth passes it, the sensor produces an output pulse.

■ A Clock with No Moving Parts

Fig. 8.5a shows a simple circuit which generates clock pulses. It has no moving parts, just three components: a resistor, a capacitor and an inverter. The inverter must have a Schmitt trigger input. The value of the resistor, 470R, is suitable for a TTL version of this circuit. Different frequencies are obtained by substituting capacitors of different values. If polarised capacitors are used, take care to observe correct polarity.

Fig. 8.5b is an equation which gives an approximate value of the frequency generated with a particular capacitor. The same equation may be used to find the approximate value of the capacitor which will give a required frequency. Fig. 8.5c gives the results of an experiment to find the frequencies actually given with various capacitors.

Quite often, the calculated frequency and the actual frequency are different. This is because capacitors have very wide tolerances. In some cases the actual value of a capacitor can be more than 20% above or below the value marked on it. To obtain an exact frequency of oscillation, some experimentation may be necessary. Different capacitors with the same marked value can be tried. Also, small value capacitors can be put in parallel with the large main capacitor to reduce a frequency which is slightly too high.

Notice that in Fig. 8.5a, a resistor connects the output of the Schmitt inverter to its input. This is another example of **feedback**. Feedback is a feature of all oscillator circuits.

Fig. 8.5   A simple clock circuit

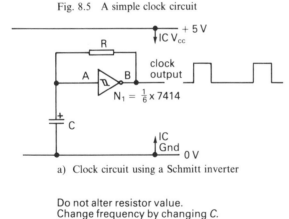

a) Clock circuit using a Schmitt inverter

Do not alter resistor value.
Change frequency by changing C.

Frequency $\approx \dfrac{2000}{C}$ Hz (if $R = 470\,R$)

(C in μF)

b) Equation for finding approximate value of frequency generated

C (μ)	$R = 470R$	
	Frequency found	Frequency calculated
0.001	1.5 MHz	2.0 MHz
0.01	167 kHz	200 kHz
0.1	16.7 kHz	20 kHz
1.0	2 kHz	2 kHz
10	200 Hz	200 Hz
470	3.6 Hz	4.3 Hz
1000	1.4 Hz	2 Hz

c) Results of an experiment to find the frequencies actually given with various capacitors

In Fig. 8.5a, when A is at logic 0, B is at logic 1, +5 V. The capacitor charges through the resistor and the voltage level at A rises. When the rising input threshold voltage is reached at A, B switches to logic 0, 0 V. The capacitor discharges through the resistor and the voltage level at A falls. When the falling input threshold voltage is reached at A, B switches back to logic 1 and the process repeats. Current flows backwards and forwards through the resistor in imitation of the pendulum movement of a mechanical clock.

The Schmitt inverter clock has a duty cycle of about 33%. The space has about twice the duration of the mark.

☐ Buffered Output

In some electronic systems, the clock circuit may have to drive a number of devices. A heavy load may upset the accuracy of the clock. Therefore it is usual to **buffer** the clock output so that the clock drives a single load, the buffer. Then the buffer drives the devices which need clock pulses. The buffer can be another inverter, as in Fig. 8.6.

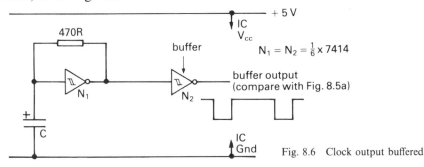

Fig. 8.6   Clock output buffered

☐ Variation on an Idea

Fig. 8.7a is an alternative version of the circuit given in Fig. 8.5a. It is built around a 4-input NAND gate with Schmitt trigger inputs, TTL 7413. As there are two gates in this chip, the second may be used as a buffer, as in Fig. 8.7b.

One of the three inputs of the buffer (Fig. 8.7b) which are tied to logic 1 ($+5$ V) could be used to control the flow of pulses from the buffer's output. If this input is at logic 1, pulses flow. If the input is at logic 0, pulses cease flowing and the buffer output is held at logic 1. Such an arrangement is called a **gated oscillator circuit**.

Fig. 8.7   Alternative Schmitt inverter clock

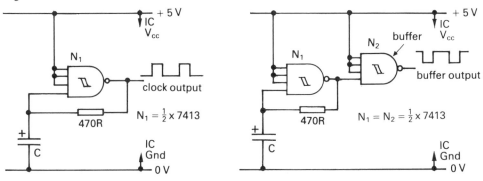

a) Clock circuit using a NAND gate with Schmitt trigger inputs

b) The clock buffered

☐ A Clock Made from Inverters

Fig. 8.8a gives another clock circuit. It uses two inverters with standard TTL inputs. The standard TTL chip, 7404, contains six suitable inverters. Inverters with Schmitt trigger inputs must not be used in this circuit.

Fig. 8.8   Another clock circuit

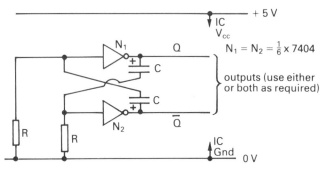

$N_1 = N_2 = \frac{1}{6} \times 7404$

outputs (use either or both as required)

a) Clock oscillator based on two inverters

C (µ)	R=1K0 Frequency (Hz)	R=2K2 Frequency (Hz)
0.1	5260	1886
1	526	175
470	1	0.35

For $R=1\text{K}0$, frequency $\simeq \dfrac{526}{C}$ Hz

For $R=2\text{K}2$, frequency $\simeq \dfrac{175}{C}$ Hz

(where C is in microfarads)

b) Results of an experiment to find the frequencies given with various capacitors and resistors

Notice the criss-cross pattern of the diagram. It is similar to the R-S flip-flop circuit. The R-S flip-flop is a **bistable system** because its outputs have two stable states, logic 0 and logic 1. The outputs remain in one or other of these states until they are made to change by an external signal. By contrast, the oscillator shown in Fig. 8.8a is an **astable system**. This means that its outputs have no stable states. If an output is at logic 0 it will, after a short interval, change to logic 1 and stay there only briefly before returning to logic 0...and so on.

The oscillator shown in Fig. 8.8a has two outputs, Q and Q-bar. They are always at opposite logic levels. Either or both of the outputs may be used as required.

The frequency of the clock is set by the two identical resistors and capacitors. If polarised capacitors are used, care must be taken to connect them correctly. The frequency is altered by changing the value of the capacitor or resistor pairs. Fig. 8.8b tabulates the results of an experiment to find the frequencies given with various capacitor and resistor pairs. Pairs of resistors in the range 1K0 to 4K7 may be used with a wide range of capacitor pairs.

Provided identical resistors and capacitors are used, this clock's pulses will have an equal mark and space. The duty cycle is 50%. Ideally, to maintain a 50% duty cycle, both of the clock outputs should be buffered even though the output from only one buffer is used. The double buffering gives both outputs the same load. If capacitors or resistors of unequal value are used, the duty cycle and the clock frequency will change.

86

■ A Clock Made from NAND Gates

In Chapter 3 we saw how an inverter may be made from a NAND gate or a NOR gate. Fig. 8.9a and Fig. 8.9b show two ways in which the previous clock circuit, made with two inverters, may be made from two NAND gates.

Fig. 8.9   A NAND gate clock

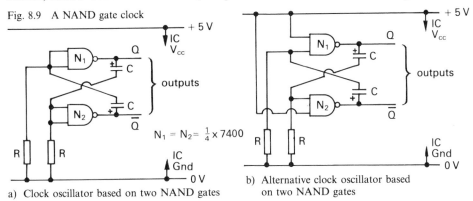

a) Clock oscillator based on two NAND gates

b) Alternative clock oscillator based on two NAND gates

$N_1 = N_2 = \frac{1}{4} \times 7400$

C (μ)	R=1K0 Frequency (Hz)	R=2K2 Frequency (Hz)
0.1	5260	2222
1	526	208
470	1	0.44

For $R=1K0$, frequency $\simeq \dfrac{526}{C}$ Hz

For $R=2K2$, frequency $\simeq \dfrac{208}{C}$ Hz

(where C is in microfarads)

c) Results of an experiment to find the frequencies given with various capacitors and resistors (both circuits)

Fig. 8.9c gives the results of an experiment to find the frequencies given with various capacitors and resistors. While the value of the capacitor pair may span a very wide range, the resistor pair should be in the range 1K0 to 4K7.

■ A Clock Made from NOR Gates

Fig. 8.10 shows two ways in which the circuit of Fig. 8.8a may be made with two NOR gates instead of the two inverters. Each circuit (Fig. 8.10a and Fig. 8.10c) gives a different frequency with identical resistor and capacitor pairs.

Fig. 8.10
A NOR
gate clock

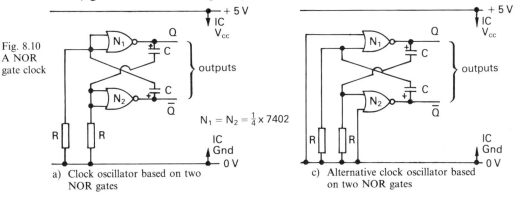

a) Clock oscillator based on two NOR gates

$N_1 = N_2 = \frac{1}{4} \times 7402$

c) Alternative clock oscillator based on two NOR gates

87

C (µ)	R=1K0 Frequency (Hz)	R=2K2 Frequency (Hz)
0.1	3704	4878
1	345	476
470	0.71	0.96

C (µ)	R=1K0 Frequency (Hz)	R=2K2 Frequency (Hz)
0.1	4761	1923
1	476	175
470	0.93	0.36

Fig. 8.10   (*continued*)

For $R=1$K0, frequency $\simeq \dfrac{345}{C}$ Hz

For $R=2$K2, frequency $\simeq \dfrac{476}{C}$ Hz

(where C is in microfarads)

b) Results of an experiment to find the frequencies given with various capacitors and resistors (Circuit a)

For $R=1$K0, frequency $\simeq \dfrac{476}{C}$ Hz

For $R=2$K2, frequency $\simeq \dfrac{175}{C}$ Hz

(where C is in microfarads)

d) Results of an experiment to find the frequencies given with various capacitors and resistors (Circuit c)

Fig. 8.10b and Fig. 8.10d are the results of experiments to find the frequencies given by various capacitors and resistors. The value of the capacitor pair may vary widely but the values of the resistor pair should be in the range 1K0 to 4K7.

■ The 555 Timer

The **555 timer** is a popular, inexpensive and versatile integrated circuit. It can function in several different ways. These are detailed in the manufacturer's or supplier's data sheets. Fig. 8.11a shows how the 555 is connected as an astable multivibrator or clock. The output frequency is given by the equation:

$$\text{output frequency (Hz)} = \frac{1.44}{(R_A + 2R_B)C}$$

where R_A and R_B are in ohms and C is in farads.

The circuit shown in Fig. 8.11a is permanently connected on the logic board together with four capacitors whose values are listed in Fig. 8.11b. Fig. 8.11b also lists the approximate frequencies produced with each capacitor and $R_A = 4$K7 and $R_B = 68$K. The frequencies are selected by wiring in the appropriate capacitor.

Some fine adjustment of the output frequency would be possible if R_B was not a single resistor but made up from a 56K resistor in series with a 22K preset, as in Fig. 8.11c. With this alteration, the value, C, of the capacitor for a required frequency is calculated with the value of R_B assumed to be 68K. When the circuit is assembled, its output frequency is measured with a frequency meter or an oscilloscope. Its value is adjusted with the 22K preset.

Fig. 8.11   A versatile circuit

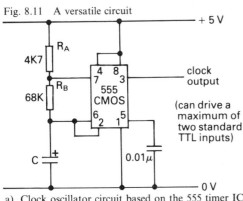

C	Frequency (Hz)
10μ	1
0.1μ	100
0.01μ	1000
1000p	10000

b) Capacitor values and resulting frequencies

a) Clock oscillator circuit based on the 555 timer IC (CMOS version)

c) R_B arranged to give frequency adjustment

There are two versions of the 555 timer. The older, cheaper one uses bipolar transistors. The newer, more expensive one uses CMOS transistors. The bipolar 555 is very useful but it creates a lot of electrical noise when running. This can prevent TTL integrated circuits from working properly. You are strongly advised not to use the bipolar 555 with logic circuits. Instead, use the low power CMOS version as used on the logic board. The output of the CMOS 555 can drive a maximum of two standard TTL inputs.

If you use a CMOS 555 timer in a project, do not solder it in place. Mount it in an **integrated circuit socket**. When handling the device, do not touch its pins or put it down on a plastic surface. CMOS devices can be damaged by the **static electricity** that can build up in our bodies and in plastic!

■   Warning Lights and Sounds

These digital microelectronic clock circuits are not suitable for use when great accuracy is needed. However, they are good general purpose circuits which can be used, for example, to drive audible alarms or flash warning lights.

Fig. 8.12 is a flashing warning lamp circuit. The clock runs continually. The AND gate controls the flow of clock pulses to the Darlington Driver. The system is a **gated oscillator**.

When input A is at logic 0, the lamp is off. Pulses from the clock cannot pass through the AND gate to the lamp. When input A is at logic 1, pulses can reach

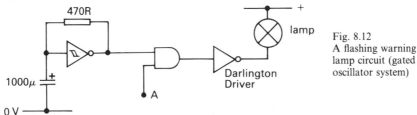

Fig. 8.12
A flashing warning lamp circuit (gated oscillator system)

89

the Darlington Driver and the lamp flashes at about 2 Hz. Any of the other clock circuits could be connected to the AND gate.

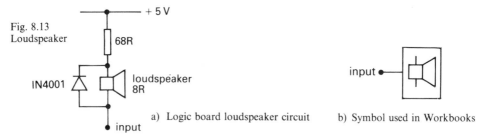

Fig. 8.13
Loudspeaker

a) Logic board loudspeaker circuit

b) Symbol used in Workbooks

Fig. 8.13a shows the loudspeaker circuit on the logic board. The 68R resistor limits the current drawn by the circuit. A reverse biased diode is connected across the coil of the loudspeaker. This protects the integrated circuits from the voltage spike produced when the coil switches off. Fig. 8.13b is the symbol for this circuit used in the assignments. The circuit must be controlled by a Darlington Driver.

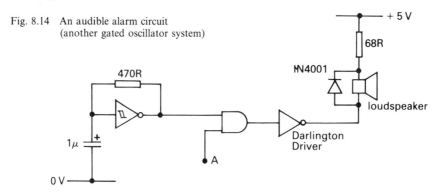

Fig. 8.14   An audible alarm circuit
(another gated oscillator system)

Fig. 8.14 is another gated oscillator system. When A is at logic 0, pulses cannot reach the Darlington Driver. No sound is produced by the loudspeaker. When A is at logic 1, the clock signal reaches the loudspeaker and a high-pitched sound is heard.

If a low frequency clock, e.g. 2 Hz, is connected to input A (Fig. 8.14), the high-pitched sound is produced in a series of bursts, beep...beep...beep...beep. This type of audible warning is more easily noticed than a continuous tone. This type of circuit is called a **tone-burst generator**.

Fig. 8.15 is the block diagram of a gated tone-burst generator system. The loudspeaker only produces a beep...beep...beep sound when A is at logic 1.

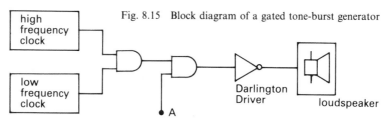

Fig. 8.15   Block diagram of a gated tone-burst generator

☐ Very Accurate Clocks

It is difficult to obtain exact frequencies from clocks which use resistors and capacitors. Also, any frequency which is obtained will not remain accurate over a long period of time.

A digital watch counts the pulses produced by a very fast oscillator. The oscillator must maintain its frequency with great accuracy if the watch is to keep correct time. To achieve this accuracy, an oscillator controlled by a **quartz crystal** is used. Many other microelectronic systems depend upon a fast, accurate clock. Fig. 8.16 shows one possible design for a crystal controlled oscillator circuit. It is the clock circuit for a microcomputer and runs at 4 MHz.

Fig. 8.16   A quartz crystal controlled oscillator circuit

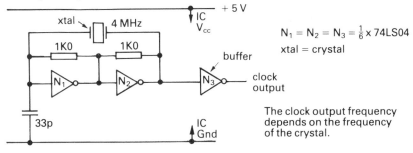

$N_1 = N_2 = N_3 = \frac{1}{6} \times$ 74LS04

xtal = crystal

The clock output frequency depends on the frequency of the crystal.

☐ Quartz Crystals

Quartz is a common mineral. It is composed of **silicon dioxide (silica)**. As a quartz crystal is strained, i.e. squashed or stretched, a voltage difference is generated across opposite faces of the crystal as shown in Fig. 8.17. This phenomenon is used in the spark igniter mechanism of a modern gas appliance. The phenomenon also works in the opposite way. If a voltage difference is applied across opposite faces of the crystal, the crystal becomes strained. This behaviour is called the **piezoelectric effect**.

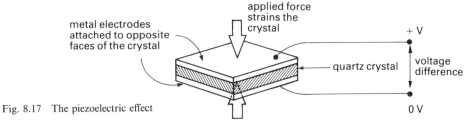

Fig. 8.17   The piezoelectric effect

When a quartz crystal is used in an electronic circuit, an applied voltage difference and the generated voltage difference interact with each other to keep the crystal continually moving from a strained to an unstrained state, i.e. the crystal oscillates at a fixed rate. There is actual, though minute, movement of the crystal. You will recall that this chapter started with a look at other clock systems which depend on movement: the pendulum system (Fig. 8.3) and the rotating disc system (Fig. 8.4).

91

A crystal's frequency of oscillation depends on its shape and size. This means that, if a crystal is carefully cut and polished, it can be made to vibrate at a frequency which is useful to an electronic engineer. Quartz crystals are available to give frequencies from about 10 kHz to well over 100 MHz.

☐ Accurate Low Frequencies

An accurate low frequency can be obtained from an accurate high frequency. The high frequency is divided down by a series of J-K flip-flops. For example, 100 Hz can be obtained from a crystal controlled oscillator running at 3.2768 MHz. This clock signal is fed into a chain of 15 J-K flip-flops as in Fig. 8.18. Each flip-flop halves the frequency. The output from the fifteenth flip-flop is a clock signal of 100 Hz, because:

$$3\ 276\ 800\ \text{Hz}/2^{15} = 100\ \text{Hz}$$

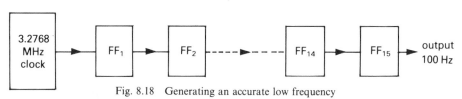

Fig. 8.18   Generating an accurate low frequency

☐ Clock Pulses from Mains Electricity

In the United Kingdom, an accurate 100 Hz clock signal can be obtained from the mains electricity supply. Mains electricity is generally supplied at 240 volts and it alternates at a frequency of 50 Hz.

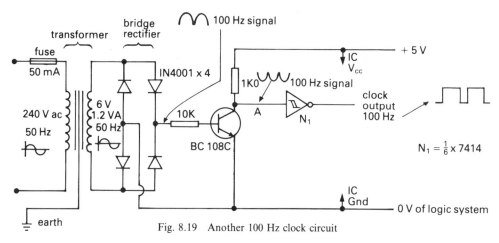

Fig. 8.19   Another 100 Hz clock circuit

In Fig. 8.19, a transformer reduces the mains voltage to 6 volts, 50 Hz. This supply is passed to a bridge rectifier. The output from the rectifier is 6 V at 100 Hz. The 100 Hz pulse stream controls the base of a transistor. A 1K0 pull-up resistor connects the collector of the transistor to a 5 V logic power supply.

92

A 100 Hz pulse stream is produced at A. The pulses are **squared up** by a Schmitt inverter before being passed on to other logic circuits.

☐ Practical Application

An accurate 100 Hz clock signal has many uses. For example, it can be used as the **timebase** of an electronic stopwatch. If the 100 Hz pulses are counted and then displayed on a calculator-type display, events which last from between 0.01 and 0.09 seconds can be timed. If flip-flops divide the 100 Hz clock by ten to give clock pulses of 10 Hz, it is possible to time events which last from between 0.01 and 0.99 seconds. The system may be extended by the addition of further **divide by ten** stages. The stopwatch outlined in Fig. 8.20 can time events which last from between 0.01 and 99.99 seconds.

Fig. 8.20   Block diagram of an electronic stopwatch

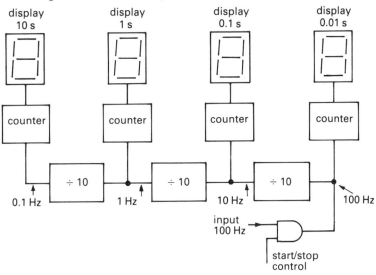

9 The 4-bit Binary Counter and Hexadecimal Display

■ Revision

Fig. 9.1 shows two cascaded J-K flip-flops. This circuit was studied in detail in Chapter 7. Fig. 9.2 shows how the outputs of these flip-flops change logic level as the circuit receives three clock pulses.

The output from the flip-flops is a binary count of the clock pulses received at the circuit's input, as in Table 9.1. The count starts at zero and its maximum is the equivalent of three in decimal. Notice that this 2-bit binary counter has a total of four different output states.

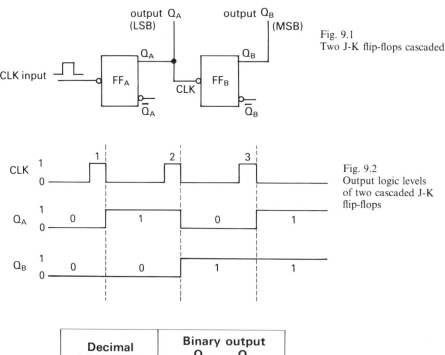

Fig. 9.1
Two J-K flip-flops cascaded

Fig. 9.2
Output logic levels of two cascaded J-K flip-flops

Decimal (CLK pulse)	Binary output Q_B 2^1	Q_A 2^0
0	0	0
1	0	1
2	1	0
3	1	1

Table 9.1   Two cascaded J-K flip-flops count the clock pulses

Fig. 9.3
A 3-bit binary count

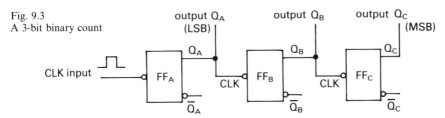

a) Three J-K flip-flops cascaded

If three J-K flip-flops are cascaded, as in Fig. 9.3a, the maximum count is extended to the equivalent of seven in decimal, as in Fig. 9.3b. A 3-bit binary counter has a total of eight output states.

Decimal (CLK pulse)	Binary output		
	Q_C 2^2	Q_B 2^1	Q_A 2^0
0	0	0	0
1	0	0	1
2	0	1	0
3	0	1	1
4	1	0	0
5	1	0	1
6	1	1	0
7	1	1	1

b) A maximum count of seven

Fig. 9.4
A 4-bit binary count

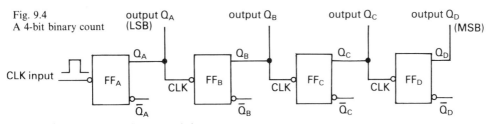

a) Four J-K flip-flops cascaded

If four J-K flip-flops are cascaded, as in Fig. 9.4a, the count can be extended to a maximum of decimal 15, as in Fig. 9.4b. A 4-bit binary counter has 16 output states.

Decimal (CLK pulse)	Binary output			
	Q_D 2^3	Q_C 2^2	Q_B 2^1	Q_A 2^0
0	0	0	0	0
1	0	0	0	1
2	0	0	1	0
3	0	0	1	1
4	0	1	0	0
5	0	1	0	1
6	0	1	1	0
7	0	1	1	1
8	1	0	0	0
9	1	0	0	1
10	1	0	1	0
11	1	0	1	1
12	1	1	0	0
13	1	1	0	1
14	1	1	1	0
15	1	1	1	1

b) A maximum count of fifteen

95

■ A 4-bit Binary Counter Chip (the 7493)

While the circuit shown in Fig. 9.4a may be constructed from two 7473 dual J-K flip-flop chips, it is more convenient to use a single chip, the 7493. This contains four J-K flip-flops, A, B, C and D as in Fig. 9.5. Flip-flops B, C and D are connected within the chip to form a 3-bit binary counter.

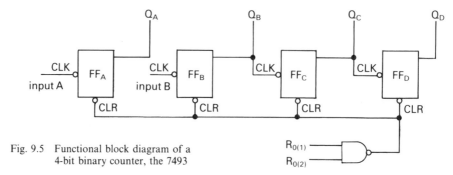

Fig. 9.5   Functional block diagram of a
4-bit binary counter, the 7493

To make a **4-bit binary counter**, the output of flip-flop A is connected externally to the clock input of flip-flop B as in Fig. 9.6. The lack of this connection internally makes the chip more useful in specialised applications.

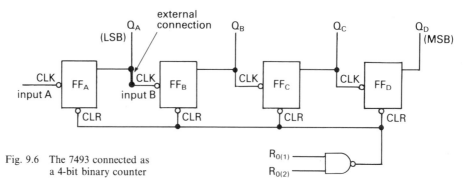

Fig. 9.6   The 7493 connected as
a 4-bit binary counter

The 7493 4-bit binary counter has four outputs, Q_A, Q_B, Q_C and Q_D. Each output can indicate a binary digit, a bit. Q_A is the least significant bit (LSB), i.e. the 2^0 or 'ones' bit. Q_D is the most significant bit (MSB), i.e. the 2^3 or 'eights' bit.

Fig. 9.7 shows the pin-out of the 7493 4-bit binary counter. Notice that the outputs, Q_A, Q_B, Q_C and Q_D, are not next to each other or in alphabetical order. Such untidiness affects many integrated circuits. Note the power supply pin numbers.

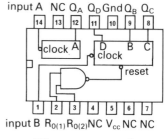

NC = not connected

Fig. 9.7   Pin-out of the 7493 4-bit
binary counter

96

■ Reset To Zero

Pins 2 and 3 of Fig. 9.7 are two reset inputs, $R_{o(1)}$ and $R_{o(2)}$. Table 9.2 shows that, if both of the reset inputs are at logic 1, the counter's outputs are reset to zero. The counter will not respond to clock pulses while the reset inputs are at logic 1. If either or both of the reset inputs are at logic 0, the counter will respond to clock pulses and the four outputs will change logic level accordingly.

Reset inputs		Output			
$R_{0(1)}$	$R_{0(2)}$	Q_D	Q_C	Q_B	Q_A
1	1	0	0	0	0
0	X		Count		
X	0		Count		

X means that the logic level can be 0 or 1.

Table 9.2   The count-reset to zero function of the 7493

■ Power-on Reset

In many applications, the counter must reset to zero when the power supply is turned on. The resistor-capacitor-inverter power-on reset circuit (Fig. 9.8) makes this happen. If required, a manual reset facility can be provided. A push-button switch and 100R resistor are added to the power-on reset circuit as in Fig. 9.8. If no reset is required, the two reset inputs, pins 2 and 3, are permanently connected to logic 0.

Fig. 9.8   Power-on and manual reset circuit for the 7493

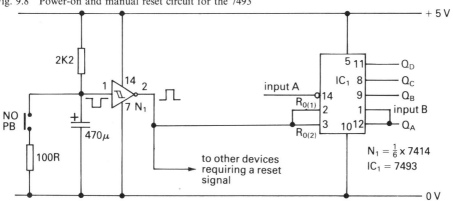

□ Know When Things Happen

A 4-bit binary counter can be used to count events, e.g. how many times a switch is operated or how many times a light beam is broken. Each operation of the switch or interruption of the light beam generates a pulse. The pulse clocks the counter.

When designing a counter, it is essential to take account of how the chip responds to clock pulses. This is so that the counter may increment at the right moment.

The 7493 increments on the negative-going edge of a clock pulse. Therefore, if the chip is presented with a positive-going pulse, as in Fig. 9.9a, the counter increments at the end of the event which generates the pulse. If the pulse is negative-going, as in Fig. 9.9b, the counter increments at the beginning of the event which generates it.

Fig. 9.9
Clock pulses

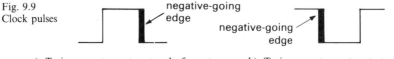

negative-going edge

negative-going edge

a) To increment counter at end of event   b) To increment counter at start of event

The clock input of the 7493 can be 'parked' at either logic level.

Clock pulses supplied to any counter must be bounce and noise free. Also, they must move rapidly between logic levels. Pulses which come from sensor circuits, e.g. for heat or light, always need to be passed through a Schmitt trigger circuit before being fed to the counter's clock input.

■ Display a 4-bit Binary Up-count

Many automatic counting systems have to display their total to people. As we saw in Chapter 1 and Activity 1, the simplest means by which a binary number can be displayed is by a row of light-emitting diodes. Fig. 9.10 shows an LED display circuit connected to the outputs of a 4-bit binary counter. Notice that the counter outputs must be connected to the LEDs through inverters. This is so that, when a counter output is at logic 0, the corresponding LED is off and, when a counter output is at logic 1, the LED is on.

Fig. 9.10
LEDs display a 4-bit
binary up-count

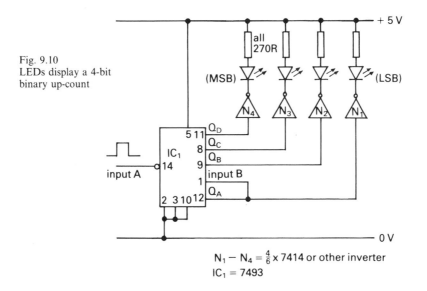

$N_1 - N_4 = \frac{4}{6} \times 7414$ or other inverter
$IC_1 = 7493$

☐ Display a 4-bit Binary Down-count

If the LEDs are driven directly by the 7493 counter, as in Fig. 9.11, a down-count is displayed even though the chip is counting up. This happens because an output at logic 0 sinks current. The LED connected to the output glows, indicating logic 1. An LED connected to an output at logic 1 does not glow. This indicates logic 0. Thus, when the counter reaches 1111, the LEDs display 0000.

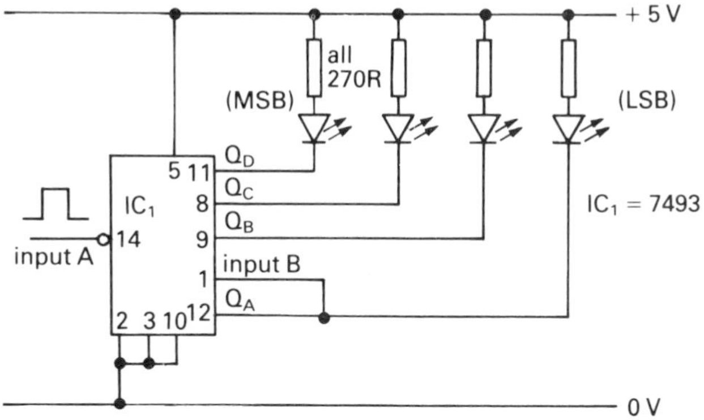

Fig. 9.11
LEDs display
a 4-bit binary
down-count

■ Display the Count in Ordinary Figures

A binary display is not easy to read quickly and accurately. It is much more convenient if a count can be displayed in ordinary figures as on a calculator. The easiest way of doing this is to use a special device, the TIL 311 display. Two of these displays are included on the logic board.

■ The TIL 311 Display

The TIL 311 display is packaged in transparent red plastic. Inside the package is an integrated circuit and 22 tiny 'dot' LEDs. The chip is just visible. It is about 2.5 mm square, silvery in colour and at the bottom of the front of the device. With good light and a magnifying glass, details can be seen.

Two of the dot LEDs indicate decimal points, one on the left and one on the right. These are not used on the logic board. The other 20 LEDs illuminate to produce well-formed, rounded figures. The LEDs are controlled by the integrated circuit. The integrated circuit is controlled by the output of a 4-bit binary counter. The LEDs illuminate to form the single figure equivalent of the counter's binary output, e.g. if the counter's output is 0101, the display indicates 5.

☐ The TIL 311 Display in Detail

Fig. 9.12 is the pin-out of the TIL 311 display. It shows its three main sections, the **latch**, the **decoder-driver** and the pattern of the LEDs. The job of

99

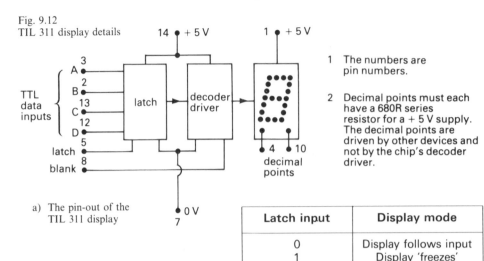

Fig. 9.12
TIL 311 display details

1 The numbers are pin numbers.

2 Decimal points must each have a 680R series resistor for a + 5 V supply. The decimal points are driven by other devices and not by the chip's decoder driver.

a) The pin-out of the TIL 311 display

Latch input	Display mode
0	Display follows input
1	Display 'freezes'

Blanking input	Display mode
0	Display on
1	Display off

b) The display function table

the decoder-driver is to receive a 4-bit binary number from the latch and turn the 20 LEDs on or off so that the correct equivalent figure is displayed. The latch inputs, A, B, C and D, are connected to the corresponding outputs of a 4-bit binary counter.

The TIL 311 has two control inputs, the **latch input** and the **blanking input**.

If the latch input is at logic 0, the display changes as the binary count changes, as in Fig. 9.12b. If the latch input is at logic 1, the display **freezes** and does not change even though the binary count continues. As soon as the latch input returns to logic 0, the display jumps to indicate the number which the count has reached. This facility is useful if the display is used, for example, in a stopwatch. It enables the user to take a spot reading of, say, the time elapsed since the start of a race.

If the blanking input is at logic 0, the display LEDs illuminate to indicate a number, as in Fig. 9.12b. If the blanking input is at logic 1, none of the LEDs illuminate. This facility might be used in a two-digit display system. There are times when the most significant digit (the left-hand digit) is 0, e.g. when the display indicates 03. The '0' is called a **leading zero**. A logic gate can be used to detect a leading zero and signal the blanking input so that it is not indicated. The display simply indicates 3. Pocket calculators are among the many devices with displays in which leading zeros are blanked.

Similarly, there are times when the least significant digit (the right-hand digit) is an unnecessary zero, e.g. in a display of a number less than 1 such as .60. The '0' is a **trailing zero**. Again, a trailing zero can be detected and blanked.

If the latching and blanking facilities are not required, these inputs are permanently connected to logic 0.

100

■ A Simple Count and Display Circuit

Fig. 9.13 shows the 7493 4-bit binary counter connected to the TIL 311 display. The circuit is in its simplest form. The counter has no reset circuit and the display's latch and blanking inputs are tied to logic 0.

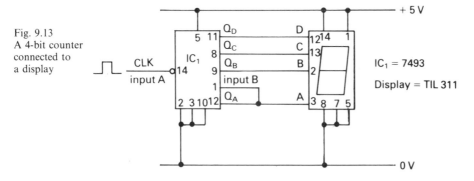

Fig. 9.13
A 4-bit counter
connected to
a display

$IC_1 = 7493$

Display = TIL 311

□ A Two Digit Display

If another counter and display are added to the circuit in Fig. 9.13, a two digit readout results, as in Fig. 9.14. The original counter and display are on the right. They give the least significant digit of the count. It is this counter which receives pulses from some source. Its Q_D output pulses the clock input of the counter on the left. This counter controls the most significant digit of the readout. If a third counter and display was required, it would be added to the left of the system in Fig. 9.14. Its clock input would be connected to the Q_D output of the second counter.

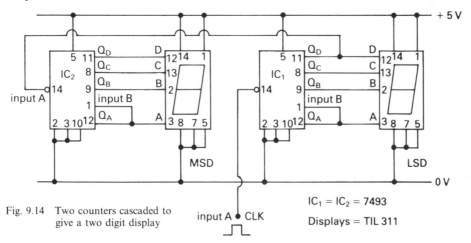

Fig. 9.14   Two counters cascaded to give a two digit display

$IC_1 = IC_2 = 7493$

Displays = TIL 311

■ A Problem

As the counter in the single display circuit (Fig. 9.13) increments, the display indicates in turn the figures 0, 1, 2, 3, 4, 5, 6, 7, 8 and 9. The binary equivalent of 9 is 1001. But, this is not the end of a 4-bit binary count. The count can

101

continue from 1001 up to 1111. The binary number after 1001 is 1010. This is the equivalent of decimal 10. But the display cannot indicate 10. Instead, it indicates A. As the count continues to its maximum of 1111, the display shows in turn the letters B, C, D, E and F. The six letters are used instead of 10, 11, 12, 13, 14 and 15. Once the maximum is reached, the count begins again from 0.

A decimal or base 10 count runs from 0 to 9 before it repeats. A count which runs from 0 to F before it repeats is a **hexadecimal (hex)** or **base 16 count**. This may seem a strange way of counting, but it is no different from counting in pounds and ounces. This is based on 16 rather than 10 and millions of people have used it for generations without difficulty (Table 9.3).

lb	oz		lb	oz
0	9		0	9
0	10		0	A
0	11		0	B
0	12	$\equiv$	0	C
0	13		0	D
0	14		0	E
0	15		0	F
1	0		1	0
1	1		1	1
etc.			etc.	

a) In the familiar decimal form   b) In hexadecimal form

Table 9.3 Pounds and ounces

■ Hexadecimal Counting

In Table 9.4, identical sections from three counting systems, binary (base 2), decimal (base 10) and hexadecimal (base 16), are set side by side for comparison.

The decimal counting system is reviewed in Table 9.5a. In Table 9.5a the decimal number 117 means

1 lot of a hundred

plus

1 lot of ten

plus

7 lots of one.

The hexadecimal counting system is reviewed in Table 9.5b. In Table 9.5b the hexadecimal number 75 means

7 lots of sixteen = 112

plus

5 lots of one = 5

Binary	Decimal	Hexadecimal
0000	0	0
0001	1	1
0010	2	2
0011	3	3
0100	4	4
0101	5	5
0110	6	6
0111	7	7
1000	8	8
1001	9	9
1010	10	A
1011	11	B
1100	12	C
1101	13	D
1110	14	E
1111	15	F

Table 9.4 Counting systems compared: binary, decimal and hexadecimal

In familiar decimal: $112 + 5 = 117$. In other words, 117 is the decimal equivalent of hexadecimal 75.

Words	hundreds	tens	units
Powers of 10	10^2	10^1	10^0
A decimal number	1	1	7

a) Decimal system

Words	sixteens	ones
Powers of 16	16^1	16^0
A hexadecimal number	7	5

b) Hexadecimal system

Table 9.5 Counting system principles

Table 9.6 shows the hexadecimal number 3FF. This number means

3 lots of two hundred and fifty-six = 768
plus
F lots (i.e. 15 lots) of sixteen = 240
plus
F lots (i.e. 15 lots) of one = 15

In decimal: $768 + 240 + 15 = 1023$. Thus, 1023 is the decimal equivalent of hexadecimal 3FF.

Words	two hundred and fifty-sixes	sixteens	ones
Powers of 16	16^2	16^1	16^0
A hexadecimal number	3	F	F

Table 9.6 The hexadecimal number 3FF

■ Binary to Hexadecimal Conversion

The largest 8-bit binary number is 1111 1111. Usually, binary numbers are written in groups of four bits (nibbles). The groups start on the right and work towards the left. This means that the largest 10-bit binary number is written 11 1111 1111. A binary number is converted to hexadecimal by replacing each group of bits with the corresponding hexadecimal number shown in Table 9.4. Thus, binary 11 1111 1111 is 3FF in hexadecimal (1023 in decimal). Binary 1111 1111 is FF in hexadecimal (255 in decimal). FF is the largest hexadecimal number that the two displays (Fig. 9.14) can indicate.

■ Decimal to Hexadecimal Conversion

Table 9.7 gives two worked examples of decimal to hexadecimal conversion. In Table 9.7a it is obvious that the result, 1A3, is a hexadecimal number. In Table 9.7b it is not obvious that 78 is a hexadecimal and not a decimal number. To avoid errors, hexadecimal numbers are almost always terminated with a capital H or preceded by an ampersand sign, &. Thus 419 decimal is 1A3H or &1A3 and 120 decimal is 78H or &78.

MSB
$419 \div 256 = 1$(hex), remainder 163
$163 \div 16 = 10$, i.e. A(hex), remainder 3
$3 \div 1 = 3$(hex), remainder 0
LSB
419 in decimal is 1A3 in hexadecimal.

a) Converting 419 (decimal) to hexadecimal

MSB
$120 \div 16 = 7$(hex), remainder 8
$8 \div 1 = 8$(hex), remainder 0
LSB
120 in decimal is 78 in hexadecimal.

b) Converting 120 (decimal) to hexadecimal

Table 9.7   Decimal to hexadecimal conversion

■ Why Use Hex?

Digital logic and computer systems carry out a great deal of binary counting. Electronic engineers and designers have to fit in with the way that binary counters work. Often, these people need to look at the numbers a system is processing. Hexadecimal notation is the easiest and most convenient way of presenting them and the necessary electronic display circuits are simple and cheap.

Another important point is that it is much easier to convert from hex to binary and back again in your head than it is to effect decimal-binary conversions.

■ A Frequency Divider

When used as a counter, the outputs of the 7493 are considered 'in parallel', i.e. as a group of outputs working together to produce a 4-bit binary number. However, the 7493 may be used as a frequency divider. In this case, the four outputs are considered individually.

A stream of pulses applied to the clock input of the counter produces pulses at each output. The frequencies of these pulses are $\frac{1}{2}$, $\frac{1}{4}$, $\frac{1}{8}$ and $\frac{1}{16}$ of the original clock frequency as in Table 9.8. In musical terms, the output frequencies are one, two, three and four octaves below the original clock frequency.

Output	Frequency
Q_A	$\frac{1}{2}$ clock
Q_B	$\frac{1}{4}$ clock
Q_C	$\frac{1}{8}$ clock
Q_D	$\frac{1}{16}$ clock

Table 9.8   A 4-bit binary counter as a frequency divider

■ A Five Tone Circuit

Fig. 9.15 shows a circuit which will produce five tones each an octave apart. Tones are selected, one at a time, by touching the plug on one of the five tone sources. It is most important that the outputs of the tone sources are not connected together by direct wiring in an attempt to hear a composite sound of two or more tones. This will destroy the frequency divider chip.

Fig. 9.15   A five octave circuit

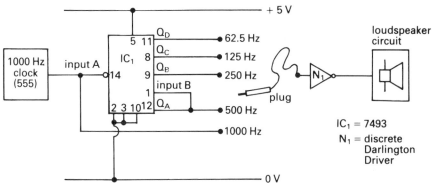

Single tones may be selected by a gating system as in Fig. 9.16. A tone is heard when its control line is at logic 1. The sound stops when the control line is at logic 0.

Fig. 9.16   A gating system for selecting tones

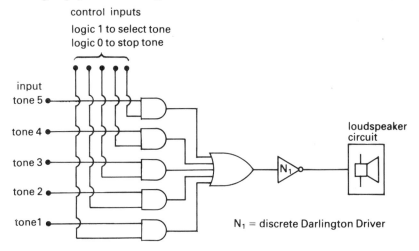

☐ Electronic Musical Instruments

It is possible to produce a composite sound made from two or more tones selected simultaneously. The outputs of the frequency divider are fed to the inputs of a summing amplifier. Here, the signals are mixed electronically. Fig. 9.17 outlines a summing circuit. It is based on a 741 operational amplifier. More than five tones may be mixed provided each one is fed to the summing point through an input resistor.

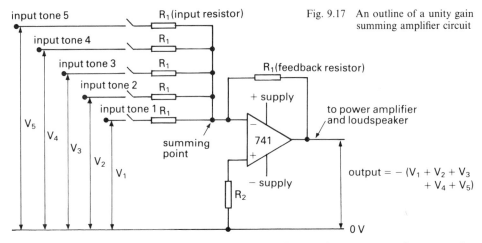

Fig. 9.17 An outline of a unity gain summing amplifier circuit

A tone generator system for a five-octave electronic organ or piano can be formed if the five-octave circuit as in Fig. 9.15 is repeated twelve times and each has an appropriate clock frequency.

To produce a fully-fledged instrument, keying, voicing, summing and power amplification systems must be designed and built. The keying system allows notes to be selected at a keyboard as required. The voicing system processes the output of the tone generator and produces different tone colours: for example, flute, clarinet and trumpet sounds. The summing circuit mixes all of the processed tones. The power amplifier receives the signal from the summing amplifier, increases its strength and drives headphones or a loudspeaker so that the instrument's sound may be heard.

A great deal of fun — and electronic knowledge — can be gained from designing and building a small electronic musical instrument, but it involves a lot of work!

☐ Divide by 16

Fig. 9.18a outlines a 4-bit binary counter circuit. The counter outputs are connected to a 4-input AND gate. The system generates one pulse at the output of the 4-input AND gate for every 16 clock pulses (Fig. 9.18b). The duration, or **width**, of the output pulse is equal to the clock period. Remember:

$$\text{clock period (s)} = 1/\text{clock frequency (Hz)}$$

Many electronic systems use circuits which generate an accurate pulse at an accurate interval. These include television transmitters and receivers and apparatus which can send information from one computer to another via a

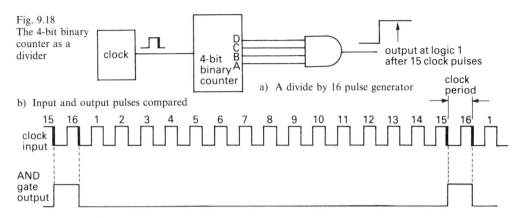

Fig. 9.18
The 4-bit binary counter as a divider

a) A divide by 16 pulse generator

output at logic 1 after 15 clock pulses

b) Input and output pulses compared

telephone line, i.e. a modem. The pulses are called **strobe** or **synchronising (sync)** pulses. Their purpose is the same as the 'left, right, left, right' shouts of a sergeant at a squad of marching soldiers. They keep the different parts of a system in step with each other so that the whole thing works properly.

☐ Time Intervals

A binary counter can be used to generate accurate time intervals. The creation of a time interval by counting is not new. Generations of children have done it when playing 'hide-and-seek'. The number is agreed beforehand. The seeker shouts to say when the count is starting and shouts again when the count is finished. In 'hide-and-seek', the count is usually up from zero. It could equally well be a count down to zero in the manner used by space craft launch controllers.

The circuit outlined in Fig. 9.19a is developed from Fig. 9.18a. A 2-input AND gate controls the flow of pulses from the 1 Hz clock to the 4-bit binary

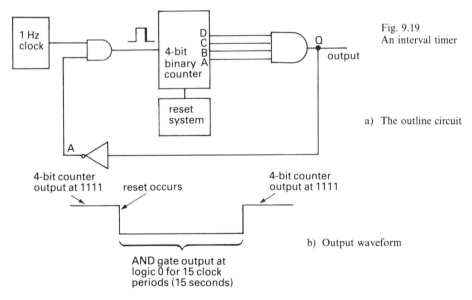

Fig. 9.19
An interval timer

a) The outline circuit

b) Output waveform

counter. This AND gate is controlled by an inverter connected to the output of the 4-input AND gate.

Imagine that the counter's output is binary 1111. Output Q of the 4-input AND gate is at logic 1. Output A of the inverter is at logic 0. The 1 Hz clock cannot pulse the counter.

Now let the counter be reset. Its output becomes binary 0000. Output Q of the 4-input AND gate is at logic 0. Inverter output A is at logic 1. The counter is pulsed by the 1 Hz clock.

Output Q of the 4-input AND gate remains at logic 0 for 15 clock periods (15 seconds). It returns to logic 1 when the counter's output is binary 1111. Inverter output A is at logic 0. The clock can no longer pulse the counter. The sequence of events is summarised in Fig. 9.19b.

The circuit outlined in Fig. 9.19a could be part of a process control system. For example, it could be used in a furniture factory to control a press which clamps freshly glued pieces of wood for a precise time.

☐ Reduce the Time

The time interval given by the system shown in Fig. 9.19 can be shortened to five seconds. The 4-input AND gate has to detect and respond to a number lower than 1111. Decimal and hexadecimal 5 are both binary 0101. If the 4-input AND gate is to respond when the counter's outputs are at 0101, it must 'see' the two binary zeros as binary 1. Two inverters make this possible. The inverters are connected to the counter's B and D outputs, as in Fig. 9.20a, as it is here that the zeros occur.

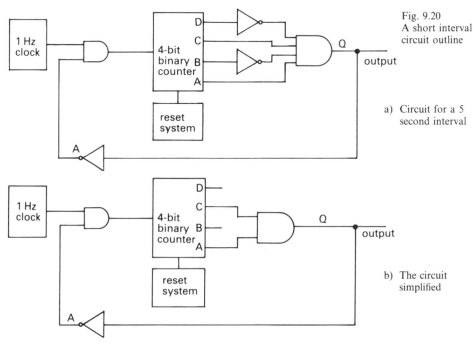

Fig. 9.20
A short interval circuit outline

a) Circuit for a 5 second interval

b) The circuit simplified

This system could be simplified. 0101 is the first time in a 4-bit binary up-count that outputs Q_A and Q_C are at logic 1 together. Therefore, the 4-input AND gate and the two inverters can be replaced by a 2-input AND gate connected to outputs Q_A and Q_C only as in Fig. 9.20b.

☐ The 74191 Presettable Up/Down Counter

In many digital microelectronic systems, a count down to zero from a chosen number is used in preference to a count up from zero to a chosen number. The reason for this is that zero is easy to detect with logic gates. More importantly, the gates do not need to be altered if the count is altered.

The different families of logic chips include binary counters which can be made to count down when clocked. These counters can be **preset**, i.e. a binary number can be loaded into the counter. When clocked, the counter counts down to zero from that number. The length of the count depends on the number loaded. In the TTL family, the 74191 chip is one of several presettable 4-bit binary counters. It can be made to count up or down as required. Fig. 9.21 shows how this device may be connected to count down from a preset number not exceeding binary 1111.

Fig. 9.21 The 74191 presettable 4-bit binary up/down counter

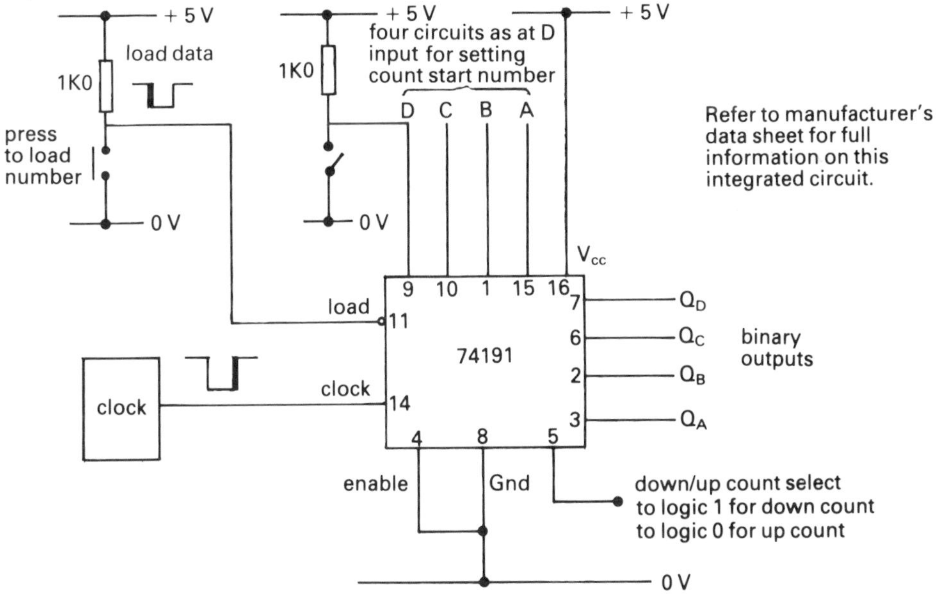

10 The Decade Counter and 7-segment Display

■ Everyday Counting

Most ordinary, everyday counting is done in decimal (base 10) and not hexadecimal (base 16). One notable exception is time-keeping. This is done in an odd mixture of base 60 and base 12 or base 24!

■ A Base 10 Count (Decimal)

It is easy to make a 4-bit binary counter count in base 10 so that a display shows only the numbers 0 to 9. To shorten the count, the counter is connected so that it resets itself to zero when it reaches the required maximum count *plus 1*.

For base 10, the maximum count is 9. 9 plus 1 makes 10. The binary equivalent of 10 is 1010. Table 10.1 shows that binary 1010 is the first time in the count that bit 1 and bit 3 are at logic 1 together. Therefore, bit 1 and bit 3 are used to generate the signal which resets the 4-bit binary counter to zero.

Fig. 10.1a shows that the 7493 4-bit binary counter resets to zero when both reset inputs are at logic 1. Therefore, if output Q_B (bit 1) and output Q_D (bit 3) are each connected to a reset input as in Fig. 10.1b, the counter will

Binary				Hexadecimal	Decimal
Bit 3 Q_D	Bit 2 Q_C	Bit 1 Q_B	Bit 0 Q_A		
0	0	0	0	0	0
0	0	0	1	1	1
0	0	1	0	2	2
0	0	1	1	3	3
0	1	0	0	4	4
0	1	0	1	5	5
0	1	1	0	6	6
0	1	1	1	7	7
1	0	0	0	8	8
1	0	0	1	9	9
1	0	1	0	A	10
1	0	1	1	B	11
1	1	0	0	C	12
1	1	0	1	D	13
1	1	1	0	E	14
1	1	1	1	F	15

Table 10.1   Binary, hexadecimal and decimal conversion table

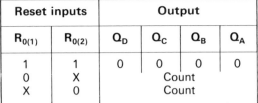

Reset inputs		Output			
$R_{0(1)}$	$R_{0(2)}$	Q_D	Q_C	Q_B	Q_A
1	1	0	0	0	0
0	X		Count		
X	0		Count		

X means that the logic level can be 0 or 1.

Fig. 10.1 A base 10 count

a) Count-reset to zero function of the 7493

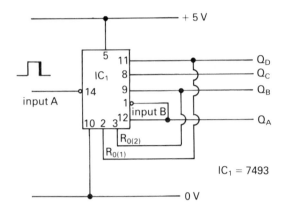

$IC_1 = 7493$

b) Reset circuit to make a 4-bit binary counter count from 0 to 9 only

reset to zero as soon as it reaches 9 plus 1, i.e. 10. The time interval between the count reaching 1010 (10 in decimal) and the counter resetting to zero is a fraction of a millionth of a second. As far as a human observer is concerned, the counter does not appear to reach 10 but seems to go instantly from 9 back to 0.

☐ A Count of Any Length (Any Base)

The method used to achieve a decimal count with a 4-bit binary counter may be used to give a count of any length. The 'binary ones' in the required maximum count plus 1 are used to generate a signal which resets the counter to zero. Examples of this are given below.

1   For a maximum count of 2 (base 3):
    2 plus 1 is 3. The binary equivalent of 3 is 0011. This is the first time in the count that bit 0 and bit 1 are at logic 1 simultaneously. Therefore outputs Q_A (bit 0) and Q_B (bit 1) are connected to a reset input each.

2   For a maximum count of 3 (base 4):
    3 plus 1 is 4. The binary equivalent of 4 is 0100. This is the first time in the count that bit 2 is at logic 1. Therefore output Q_C (bit 2) is connected to both of the reset inputs.

Some counts can be achieved only with the help of an AND gate. For example, a maximum count of 6 is required (base 7). 6 plus 1 is 7. The binary

111

equivalent of 7 is 0111. This is the first time in the count that bits 0, 1 and 2 are at logic 1 simultaneously. Output Q_A (bit 0), output Q_B (bit 1) and output Q_C (bit 2) must be connected to the inputs of a 3-input AND gate. The output of the AND gate is connected to both of the reset inputs as in Fig. 10.2.

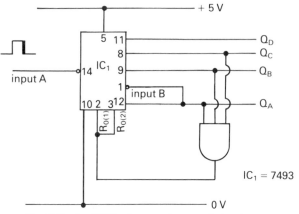

An alternative solution is to connect output Q_C to one reset input. Outputs Q_A and Q_B are connected to the inputs of a 2-input AND gate. The output of the AND gate is connected to the other reset input.

Fig. 10.2   An AND gate generates a reset signal

■ The 7490 Decade Counter

When a decimal count is required, it is convenient to use the TTL 7490 **decade counter** as in Fig. 10.3. One is included on the logic board. This chip is a 4-bit binary counter with internal reset connections which shorten its count to the binary equivalent of 9.

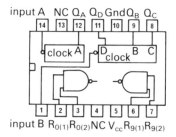

Fig. 10.3   Pin-out of the 7490 decade counter

The 7490 decade counter contains four J-K flip-flops arranged in two blocks. One block is a single flip-flop, A. The other block contains three connected flip-flops, B, C and D, as in Fig. 10.3. The two block arrangement allows designers to use the decade counter in a variety of ways.

When used as a decade counter, output Q_A must be connected externally to input B as in Fig. 10.4. Input A receives clock signals from some source. The 7490 counter increments on the negative-going edge of a clock pulse. Outputs Q_A, Q_B, Q_C and Q_D drive a display. The display could be the TIL 311 device used earlier with the 4-bit binary counter.

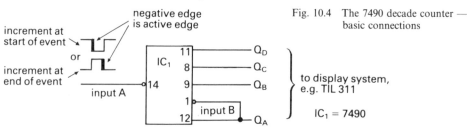

Fig. 10.4   The 7490 decade counter — basic connections

112

The 7490 decade counter has two pairs of reset inputs, as in Fig. 10.3. One pair, at pins 2 and 3, resets the counter to zero. The other pair, at pins 6 and 7, resets the counter to binary 9.

The reset to 9 inputs are used in specialised applications. If they are not going to be used, they must be permanently connected to logic 0. If these connections are not made, the counter will not operate.

Table 10.2 sets out the count-reset function of the 7490. This table is a little complicated but simplification is possible.

Reset inputs				Output				
$R_{0(1)}$	$R_{0(2)}$	$R_{9(1)}$	$R_{9(2)}$	Q_D	Q_C	Q_B	Q_A	
1	1	0	X	0	0	0	0	X means that
1	1	X	0	0	0	0	0	the logic level
X	X	1	1	1	0	0	1	can be 0 or 1.
X	0	X	0	Count				
0	X	0	X	Count				
0	X	X	0	Count				
X	0	0	X	Count				

Table 10.2 The count-reset function of the 7490

If we forget about reset to 9 and extract from Table 10.2 information dealing with reset to zero, we obtain Table 10.3. This table is identical to the count-reset to zero table for the 7493 4-bit binary counter given in Chapter 9.

The power-on and manual reset to zero methods used with the 7493 binary counter can be used with the 7490 decade counter.

Reset inputs		Output				
$R_{0(1)}$	$R_{0(2)}$	Q_D	Q_C	Q_B	Q_A	
1	1	0	0	0	0	X means that the
0	X	Count				logic level can
X	0	Count				be 0 or 1.

Table 10.3 The count-reset to zero function of the 7490

Reset connections may be made so that the 7490 decade counter gives a maximum count of less than 9. Again, the method is identical to that used with the 7493 4-bit binary counter.

■ An Alternative Display

The TIL 311 display is a very good and convenient device. However, it is expensive. A cheaper alternative is a **7-segment display**. It is ideal when a decimal display is required. It is used widely in watches and calculators.

The segments are arranged as shown in Fig. 10.5a. Each segment is identified by a lower-case letter as in Fig. 10.5b.

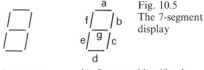

Fig. 10.5
The 7-segment display

a) 7-segment pattern

b) Segment identification letters

The 7-segment Display

Fig. 10.6 shows the digits formed by a 7-segment display. Sometimes the 6 and the 9 have tails as shown. Check the 6 and 9 on your watch or calculator.

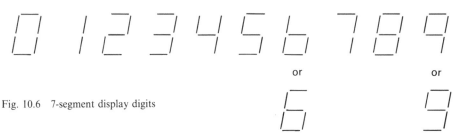

Fig. 10.6 7-segment display digits

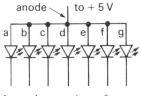

or

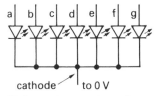

or

The segments can be like **light bulb filaments**. These displays are fitted to many petrol pumps.

The segments may be liquid crystals. These become dark and opaque when indicating a digit. **Liquid crystal displays (LCDs)** use a minute amount of electric current and are ideal for battery-powered equipment such as watches and calculators. However, the digits cannot be seen in the dark as they do not glow. They are seen by reflected light.

The segments can be **light-emitting diodes (LEDs)**.

Light-emitting Diode 7-segment Displays

Seven-segment LED displays are manufactured with two types of internal connection, common anode (CA) and common cathode (CC), as in Fig. 10.7. Common cathode LED displays are used with devices which source current. Common anode LED displays are used with devices which sink current. It is essential that a display matches the device which is to control it.

Fig. 10.7
Two types of LED
7-segment display

a) Internal connections of a common anode (CA) display

b) Internal connections of a common cathode (CC) display

In addition to the seven segments, the displays usually have one or even two extra LEDs for use as decimal points, one on the left and one on the right. If they are not required, they are left unconnected.

114

The pin-out of the segments varies considerably between displays. Also, it may be necessary to make more than one connection to the +5 V or 0 V rails. It is essential that manufacturers' data sheets are consulted.

■ Current-limiting Resistors

Each individual LED in a 7-segment display must be in series with a **current-limiting resistor** as in Fig. 10.8. The current-limiting resistors may be the familiar discrete components or they may be seven separate resistors contained in one integrated circuit package called a **resistor network**. Data sheets recommend resistor values or give guidance for their calculation.

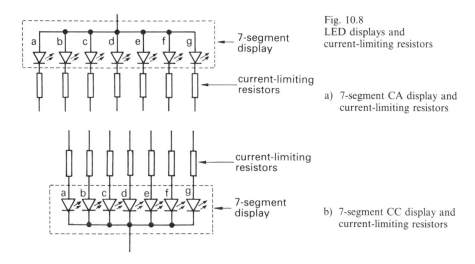

Fig. 10.8
LED displays and
current-limiting resistors

a) 7-segment CA display and
   current-limiting resistors

b) 7-segment CC display and
   current-limiting resistors

□ Incandescent Displays

An easy-to-use alternative to the 7-segment LED display and its current-limiting resistors is a display with seven incandescent filaments. Sometimes they are called 'Minitron' displays. If used in a system with a +5 V supply they do not require current-limiting resistors. They may be connected by the user in common anode or common cathode form. Always check that the device which is to control the display can handle the current drawn by each segment. Incandescent displays are more expensive than LED displays and are more fragile as the filaments are sealed under a glass cover.

■ Binary Coded Decimal to 7-Segment Decoder Driver

Because a 7-segment display with series resistors has seven inputs, it cannot be connected directly to a decade counter which has only four outputs. The two must be interfaced with a special integrated circuit as in Fig. 10.9. This chip has four inputs which accept the binary count and seven outputs which

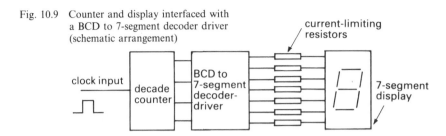

Fig. 10.9   Counter and display interfaced with
a BCD to 7-segment decoder driver
(schematic arrangement)

control the LEDs. The interface chip makes the LEDs turn on or off so that
the display indicates the 0 to 9 equivalent of the binary count. The interface
integrated circuit is called a **binary coded decimal (BCD) to 7-segment decoder
driver**.

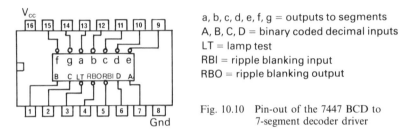

a, b, c, d, e, f, g = outputs to segments
A, B, C, D = binary coded decimal inputs
LT = lamp test
RBI = ripple blanking input
RBO = ripple blanking output

Fig. 10.10   Pin-out of the 7447 BCD to
7-segment decoder driver

Fig. 10.10 is the pin-out of the TTL 7447 binary coded decimal to 7-
segment decoder driver. The 7447 chip can drive only common anode (CA)
LED or incandescent displays.

Fig. 10.11   Display circuit diagram

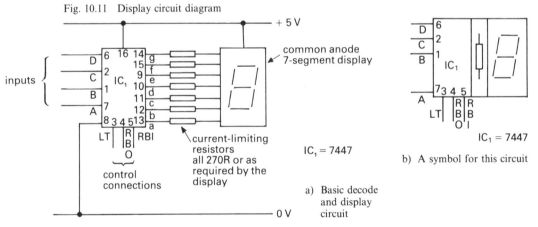

Fig. 10.11a shows the basic connections of a decode and display circuit. This
circuit is permanently connected on the logic board. Fig. 10.11b is a symbol
for the circuit. The symbol is used in the Workbook to avoid confusion
between the permanent connections and the connections you have to make.
In your written work, always draw the full circuit diagram.

In Fig. 10.11a, the A, B, C and D inputs of the 7447 connect directly to
outputs Q_A, Q_B, Q_C and Q_D of a 7490 decade counter. The a, b, c, d, e, f and g

116

outputs of the 7447 are connected by current-limiting resistors to the corresponding segments of a display as in Fig. 10.5b.

The 7447 chip has three control connections, LT, RBI and RBO. These are explained later.

■ Basic Decade Count, Decode and Display Circuits

Fig. 10.12 shows a single digit decade count, decode and display circuit. It can count from 0 to 9. If a second, identical, circuit is placed on the left of this circuit, a 0 to 99 count can be obtained (Fig. 10.13).

Fig. 10.12   Single digit count and display circuit

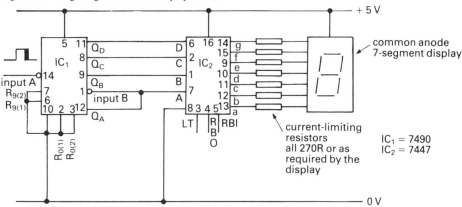

Fig. 10.13   Decade counters cascaded to give a multidigit display

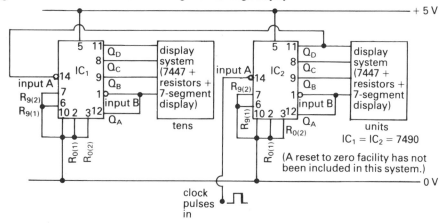

In Fig. 10.13, the units counter receives clock pulses from some source. The tens counter is clocked by the Q_D output of the units counter.

Both of the circuits as in Fig. 10.12 and Fig. 10.13 need a reset to zero system if they are to be of use. Neither circuit uses the 7447 control connections and, in many applications, this does not matter.

□ 7447 Control Connections

The 7447 decoder-driver has three control connections. Two are inputs and one is an output. They are:

$$LT = \text{Lamp Test (pin 3)}$$
$$RBI = \text{Ripple Blanking Input (pin 5)}$$
$$RBO = \text{Ripple Blanking Output (pin 4).}$$

The LT input, pin 3, provides means by which the 7447 outputs and the display can be checked. Normally, the LT input is at logic 1. But, if the LT input is taken to logic 0, all other inputs are ignored and all of the segments of the display should illuminate. If they do not, there is something wrong with either the display or the chip.

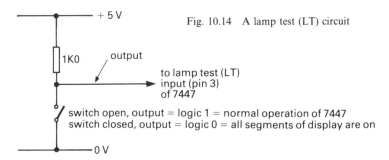

Fig. 10.14   A lamp test (LT) circuit

Fig. 10.14 gives a lamp test circuit. It may be connected to the LT input of several 7447 chips so that a complete display system may be tested by operation of a single switch. If a lamp test facility is not required, all LT inputs should be connected permanently to logic 1.

In many systems, the RBI input, pin 5, may be connected permanently to logic 1 and forgotten. However, it can be used to refine the appearance of a display.

If the RBI input is held at logic 0, the display is blank when the A, B, C and D inputs are at logic 0. There are two outcomes: one is that the display will never show a zero, which is useful for leading and trailing zero blanking; and the other is that the RBO output, pin 4, goes to logic 0 while these input conditions exist.

The RBO output, pin 4, can control the RBI input of another decoder-driver. This makes it possible to blank several leading or trailing zeros in a multidigit display.

Fig. 10.15 shows the connections required to blank two leading zeros in a three digit display. Instead of displaying for example, '030' it will show '30'. Instead of displaying '002' it will show '2'. Instead of displaying '000' it will show '0'. This latter is possible because there is no RBO-RBI connection between the tens decoder-driver and the units decoder-driver.

In a display of decimal fractions — tenths, hundredths, thousandths, etc. — trailing zeros may be blanked as in Fig. 10.16. Thus, instead of displaying

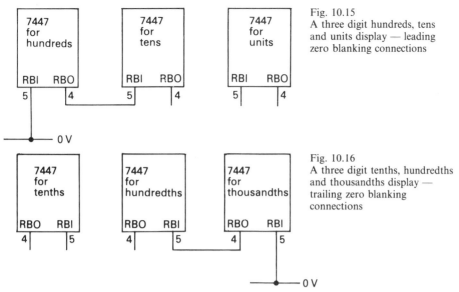

Fig. 10.15
A three digit hundreds, tens and units display — leading zero blanking connections

Fig. 10.16
A three digit tenths, hundredths and thousandths display — trailing zero blanking connections

'030' it will show '03'. Instead of displaying '200' it will show '2'. Instead of displaying '000' it will show '0'.

□ Some Multidigit Display Circuits

Fig. 10.17 gives the circuit for a two digit tens and units count and display

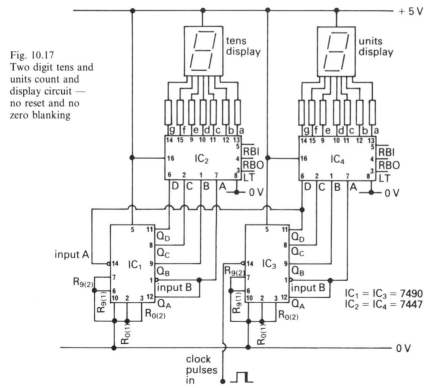

Fig. 10.17
Two digit tens and units count and display circuit — no reset and no zero blanking

$IC_1 = IC_3 = 7490$
$IC_2 = IC_4 = 7447$

119

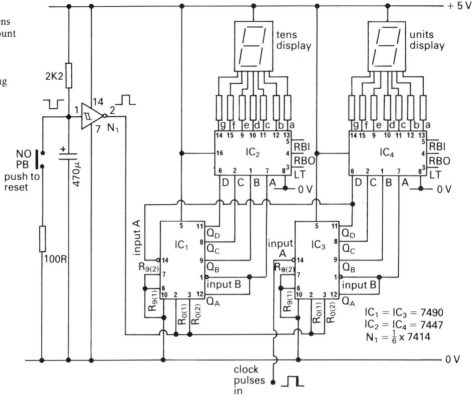

Fig. 10.18
Two digit tens
and units count
and display
circuit with
reset — no
zero blanking

$IC_1 = IC_3 = 7490$
$IC_2 = IC_4 = 7447$
$N_1 = \frac{1}{6} \times 7414$

system. This is the simplest system. There is no reset to zero facility and no arrangements have been made to blank a leading zero.

Fig. 10.18 adds power-on and manual reset facilities to the circuit given in Fig. 10.17. If the power-on reset is not required, the capacitor must be removed. If the manual reset is not required, the push-button and 100R resistor are removed.

Fig. 10.19 adds leading zero blanking to the circuit given in Fig. 10.17. Leading zero blanking is easily provided on a three digit hundreds, tens and units count and display system. The method is outlined in Fig. 10.15.

The circuit given in Fig. 10.17 can serve as a tenths and hundredths count and display system. In this case it may be desirable to blank a trailing zero. The circuit given in Fig. 10.20 shows how this is done. Trailing zero blanking is easily provided on a three digit tenths, hundredths and thousandths count and display system. The method is outlined in Fig. 10.16.

□ What If...?

If the 7447 BCD to 7-segment decoder driver is driven by a 4-bit binary counter instead of a decade counter, it will display the digits 0 to 9. Above 9 it will not display the digits A to F but meaningless squiggles. When the input is binary 1111, the display is blank.

When a 7-segment display is used with a suitable decoder to give a

120

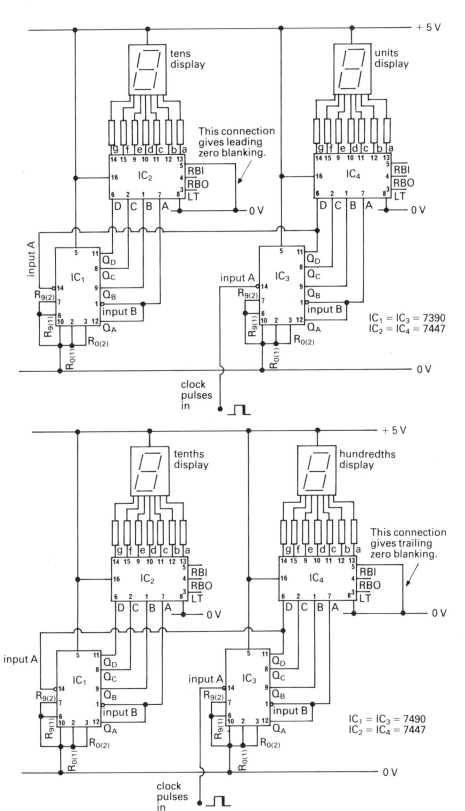

Fig. 10.19
Two digit tens and units count and display circuit with leading zero blanking — no reset

Fig. 10.20
Two digit tenths and hundredths count and display circuit with trailing zero blanking — no reset

121

Fig. 10.21 7-segment indication of the digits A to F

hexadecimal display, the letters A to F are presented in a mixture of upper and lower case letters as in Fig. 10.21. Care must be taken when reading such a display as it is very easy to confuse b and 6.

☐ Divide a Frequency by 10

The 7490 decade counter may be used to divide a frequency by 10. The process is in two parts. First, the frequency is divided by 5 by the B, C and D block of flip-flops. Then, it is divided by 2 by the A flip-flop. Division in this manner means that the output waveform is symmetrical: the mark and the space times are equal.

The 7490 is connected, as in Fig. 10.22, in a manner different from that seen previously. The frequency to be divided is supplied to input B. Output Q_D is connected to input A. Output Q_A produces the original frequency divided by ten. Outputs Q_B, Q_C and Q_D are not used.

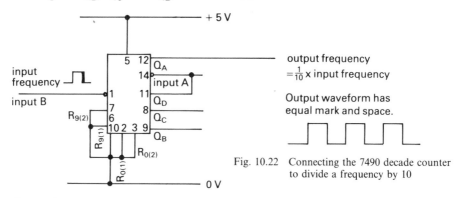

Fig. 10.22 Connecting the 7490 decade counter to divide a frequency by 10

Several 7490 decade counters may be cascaded to divide a frequency by 100 or 1000 and so on. When cascading, output Q_A of one frequency divider is connected to input B of the next divider.

☐ A Reaction Timer — a Worked Example in Circuit Design

The Problem
When a signal light is switched on by one person, another person has to switch on a response light. The response must be made as quickly as possible. The time interval between the signal and the response light turning on is to be measured electronically. Outline a circuit design.

☐ Timer

Basically, the system is a timer. The timer starts when the signal light turns on. The timer stops when the response light turns on.

122

The timer is a clock circuit which produces a known number of pulses in a given time. The 555 timer circuit might be used. The pulses are counted. The count gives the time interval.

Before the timer can be outlined, more information is required:

Question What is the maximum length of time to be measured?
Answer One second.

Question What accuracy of measurement is required?
Answer Measure to the nearest 0.01 of a second.

Question What timebase is required?
Answer A 100 Hz clock. The clock pulses will be counted and the total displayed. The total is the response time.

Question How many counters and displays are required?
Answer Two of each so that 0.01 s and 0.1 s can be counted and displayed. The maximum time displayed is 0.99 s.

Fig. 10.23 is a block diagram which shows the essential parts of a two digit timer. It can measure intervals of up to 0.99 s in increments of 0.01 s.

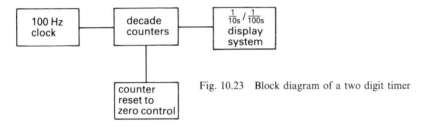

Fig. 10.23   Block diagram of a two digit timer

□   **Switches and Lights**

Fig. 10.24 is a block diagram which defines the switch and light sections of the system. When the signal switch turns on the signal light, timing must begin from zero. When the response switch turns on the response light, timing must stop.

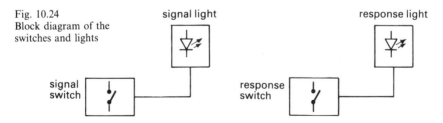

Fig. 10.24
Block diagram of the
switches and lights

The lights can be LEDs. They can have logic board 8-bit indicator circuitry. The switches can be slide switches. They can have the logic 0-logic 1 circuitry used by the 8-bit switch on the logic board.

☐ Linking the Sections

The two switch and light systems have to be linked to the timer. Some form of gating is necessary. Fig. 10.25 is a block diagram which shows the relationship of the various parts of the reaction timer system.

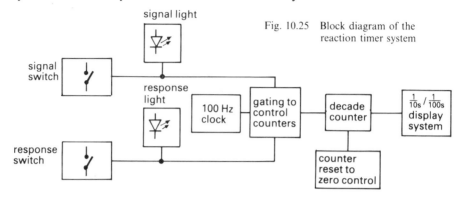

Fig. 10.25 Block diagram of the reaction timer system

☐ Designing the Gating

The signal switch function is:

signal switch at logic 0 = signal light off, clock pulses blocked;
signal switch at logic 1 = signal light on, clock pulses pass to counter.

Fig. 10.26 Signalling system requirements

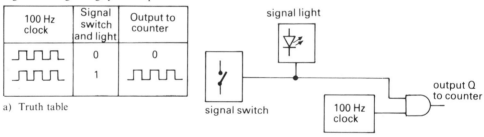

100 Hz clock	Signal switch and light	Output to counter
⎍⎍⎍	0	0
⎍⎍⎍	1	⎍⎍⎍

a) Truth table

b) The signal switch — clock gating system

These requirements are summarised in the truth table in Fig. 10.26a. They are met by an AND gate as in Fig. 10.26b. The circuit is the same as the gated oscillator in Chapter 8.

The response switch function is:

response switch at logic 0 = response light off, clock pulses from Q
(Fig. 10.26b) pass to counter;
response switch at logic 1 = response light on, clock pulses from Q blocked.

This is summarised in the truth table in Fig. 10.27a.

The relationship of the response switch and the pulses from Q is the opposite of the signal switch and clock relationship. But, if the output from the response switch is inverted, it can then control the flow of pulses from Q through an AND gate, as in Fig. 10.27b.

Fig. 10.27 The response system requirements

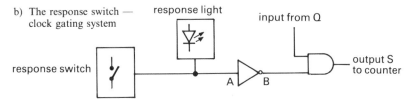

100 Hz clock pulses from Q	Response switch and light	Output to counter
⎍⎍⎍⎍	0	⎍⎍⎍⎍
⎍⎍⎍⎍	1	0

a) Truth table

Response switch and light	A	B	100 Hz input from Q	Output S to counter
0	0	1	⎍⎍⎍⎍	⎍⎍⎍⎍
1	1	0	⎍⎍⎍⎍	0

c) Truth table for the gating system

b) The response switch —
    clock gating system

Fig. 10.27c is a truth table for this gating system. Compare its first and last columns with the response switch function set out in Fig. 10.27a.

☐ The Complete Scheme

Fig. 10.28 is a schematic diagram of the reaction timer. The design has reached the point where a full circuit diagram may be drawn. The diagram would bring together many of the systems described in this and earlier chapters.

Once the circuit diagram is drawn, the circuit can be connected and tested on the logic board. Tests would, for example, assess the accuracy of the 100 Hz clock. Modifications might be considered, for example, should a clock of greater accuracy be used, is leading zero blanking desirable? Finally, when modifications have been designed, incorporated and evaluated, a permanent circuit could be built, housed and used.

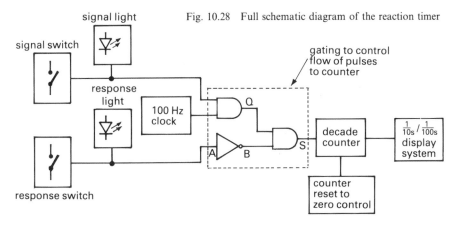

Fig. 10.28 Full schematic diagram of the reaction timer

11 Memory

Shopping List

Every day, all of us use many different memory systems. By no means are all of them electronic. Whatever they are, all memory systems store information (**data**) and **instructions**.

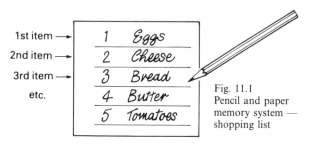

1st item → 1 Eggs
2nd item → 2 Cheese
3rd item → 3 Bread
etc. 4 Butter
5 Tomatoes

Fig. 11.1
Pencil and paper memory system — shopping list

A simple memory system is a sheet of paper with squiggles of graphite written on it with a pencil. The data stored, for example, could be a shopping list, as in Fig. 11.1. Anyone who can read English will find the squiggles meaningful.

Three Key Words

The shopping list highlights three key words used with electronic memories:

1 the list is used to **store** data;
2 someone has to **write** the data in an appropriate language;
3 someone who knows the language can **read** the data.

Locations and Addresses

The list is written line by line on a piece of paper. A longer piece of paper would have more lines and could carry a longer list. An electronic memory has its equivalent of lines. They are called **memory locations**. Some memories have more locations than others. Each location is numbered. This number is the **address** of the location. The address of the first location in an electronic memory is always zero. If the shopping list was set out with its lines numbered like an electronic memory it would be as shown in Fig. 11.2.

	Address	Data
1st location →	0	Eggs
2nd location →	1	Cheese
3rd location →	2	Bread
etc.	3	Butter
	4	Tomatoes

Fig. 11.2
Shopping list set out like an electronic memory

Addressing a Memory

If you point with your finger at location 3 (where the stored data are 'butter') on the list in Fig. 11.2, you are, in electronic terms, **addressing a memory location**.

A counter is used to address electronic memory locations. It **points** to a location by presenting the memory with a binary number. In 8-bit binary, the address of location 3, as in Fig. 11.2, is 0000 0011. Because binary numbers are inconvenient for people, we usually quote addresses in hexadecimal. The hexadecimal equivalent of address 0000 0011 is 03H (&03).

Address Pins and Memory Size

An electronic memory integrated circuit always has **address pins**. If there are eight address pins, they are numbered A0 to A7. The highest address in this memory is 1111 1111, FFH. This is equivalent to decimal 255. This memory

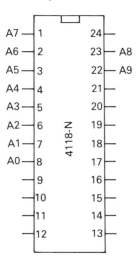

has $255 + 1 = 256$ locations (remember, the first location has address 00). If the memory has more than 256 locations, it will have more address pins. The memory integrated circuit on the logic board has ten address pins numbered A0 to A9 as in Fig. 11.3. The highest address in this memory is 11 1111 1111, &3FF. This is equivalent to decimal 1023. The memory has $1023 + 1 = 1024$ locations. This is known as a 1K memory. A memory with 256 locations is a $\frac{1}{4}$K memory.

Fig. 11.3   Memory IC address pin-out

Words and Word Length

On the shopping list in Fig. 11.1, the data are stored as graphite squiggles. We recognise them as English words for various foods.

In an electronic memory, we can think of the stored data as sets of binary numbers. An electronic system recognises them as **words** which mean something.

Memories differ not only in the number of locations they have. They differ also in the length of the binary word which can be stored in a location. In some memories, a word is just a single binary digit, a bit. In others, a word is four bits long, a nibble. Other memories, like the one on the logic board, store words eight bits long, a byte. We say that this memory is organised as:

1024 words × 8 bits.

■ Data Pins

An electronic memory integrated circuit always has **data pins**. The number of pins is equal to its word length. Data enter and leave the memory through these pins. Sometimes there are two sets of data pins, one for data input and another for data output. Sometimes the same pins are used for both data input and output. This is the case for the memory on the logic board. As the memory has an 8-bit word length, there are eight data pins numbered D0 to D7 (Fig. 11.4).

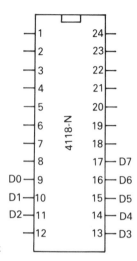

Fig. 11.4 Memory IC data pin-out

■ Sample

Table 11.1 gives the addresses of the first few locations of the memory on the logic board and some sample data. In Table 11.1a, the binary form shows the way in which the addresses and data are seen by the memory. Table 11.1b gives the same addresses and data in hexadecimal form. This is more convenient for us to read. What the data mean does not matter. Just see them as a list of words written in a foreign language which you do not understand.

The shopping list in Fig. 11.1 can be read any number of times without affecting the squiggles made by the pencil. Similarly, the data stored by an electronic memory can be read any number of times without the data being affected.

Address	Data
00 0000 0000	0010 0011
00 0000 0001	1101 1111
00 0000 0010	1000 1000
00 0000 0011	0001 1001
00 0000 0100	1010 0101

a) Addresses and data, binary

Address	Data
000	2 3
001	D F
002	8 8
003	1 9
004	A 5

b) The same addresses and data, hexadecimal

Table 11.1   Addresses and data

■ Control Pins

A memory integrated circuit has several **control pins**, $\overline{OE}$, $\overline{WE}$ and $\overline{CE}$, as in Fig. 11.5. They must be held at the right logic level when writing data into the memory or reading data from it.

OE means **output enable**. This is an **active low** input. When it is at logic 0,

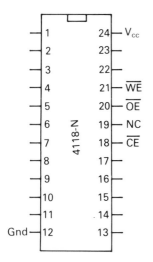

Fig. 11.5 Memory IC control pin-out

the data pins become outputs. Data can be read from the memory. When it is at logic 1, the data pins become inputs. Data can be written into the memory.

Before new data are presented at the data pins for writing into the memory, it is essential that $\overline{OE}$ is taken to logic 1 so that the data pins become inputs. This prevents a conflict between the old data already in the memory and the new data being presented to it. A conflict may damage the memory.

$\overline{WE}$ means **write enable**. The bar over the $\overline{WE}$ means that it too is an active low input. It is held at logic 1 when data are being read from the memory. It is momentarily pulsed to logic 0 to write data into the memory.

Sometimes we go shopping with two separate shopping lists. As we can only deal with one thing at a time, we leave one list isolated in a pocket while we look at the other. In a similar manner, an electronic system may have two or more memories. It too can only deal with one thing at a time. The electronic system has to isolate memories it does not want to look at. This is where the $\overline{CE}$ control pin comes in.

$\overline{CE}$ means **chip enable**. It is an active low input. When it is at logic 0, the memory chip is **enabled** and being used by the rest of the system. When $\overline{CE}$ is at logic 1, the memory chip is **disabled** and is isolated from the system.

NC means **not connected**. The memory integrated circuit requires 23 connections but is put in a standard 24-pin package. Pin 19 is a surplus pin.

The pin marked V_{cc} is for the $+5$ V power supply. The pin marked Gnd is for the 0 V or 'ground' connection.

■ Random Access Memory (RAM)

A shopping list written with pencil is easily altered. We could rub out, say, 'tomatoes' and write 'potatoes' instead. In some electronic memories, the stored data are equally easy to alter. An 'electronic rubber' is not needed. New data written in a memory location automatically removes the old data. This type of memory is called a **random access memory**, **RAM**, though a name like **read-write memory** would describe it better. The memory on the logic board is a RAM.

RAM is used in a calculator to store the results of calculations. It is also used in a computer to store, say, a games program which has been written into it from a cassette tape.

A RAM will retain data as long as its power supply is connected. It 'forgets' everything if the power is turned off even for a fraction of a second.

129

When first powered, the locations in a RAM are not empty like a blank sheet of paper. Every location contains a binary number. What the numbers are is a matter of chance. They are 'electronic scribble' and do not mean anything. They are usually called **garbage**. As data are written into the memory, the garbage is replaced by numbers which do mean something.

■ Read Only Memory (ROM)

A shopping list written in ink cannot be altered. Once written, the list can only be read. Some electronic memories are like this. This type of memory is a **read only memory**, **ROM**. When a ROM has data written into it, permanent physical changes occur in the integrated circuit. Because the changes are physical, data are not forgotten or **lost** when the power supply is turned off.

A ROM is used in a calculator. It contains the information which tells the machine what to do when any key is pressed. A ROM is also used in a computer. It contains the information which, for example, tells the computer how to write data into a RAM from a cassette tape.

■ EPROM

There is an electronic memory which is 'in-between' a RAM and a ROM. It is an **erasable programmable read only memory**, **EPROM**. Data are written into an EPROM with the help of a special 25 V power supply. The process is called **programming the memory**. The data are stored in the form of electric charges in minute capacitors. The data are not lost when the power supply is turned off. In this respect, the EPROM is like a ROM. However, data in the EPROM can be removed or **erased** by shining short wavelength ultra-violet, UV, light through a quartz window which covers its integrated circuit. The UV light discharges the capacitors. This process is called **washing an EPROM**. It takes about ten minutes. Every location is left full of binary ones. New data can then be written into the memory.

Short wavelength UV light can seriously damage eyes. A UV source should not be switched on unless it is properly enclosed in a container. The UV sources used in discos and physics laboratories are not suitable for EPROM washing.

Sometimes an opaque label is stuck over the quartz window of an EPROM. This is to prevent accidental erasure of data by sunlight or artificial light. Direct sunlight will erase an EPROM in a week. Room-level fluorescent lighting will erase an EPROM in three years.

EPROMs are very useful in electronic systems which are being developed. Data are retained when the power supply is off and yet, with the right equipment, data are very easily altered. When all tests and experiments are finished, the data in the EPROM may be transferred to a ROM.

■ Logic Board Memory

The memory integrated circuit on the logic board is a 4118-N static random access memory, RAM. Fig. 11.6 gives its pin-out and other details. **Access time 250 ns** means the time interval between a memory location being addressed and the data in that location appearing at the data pins. 250 ns (ns = nanoseconds) is 250×10^{-9} seconds.

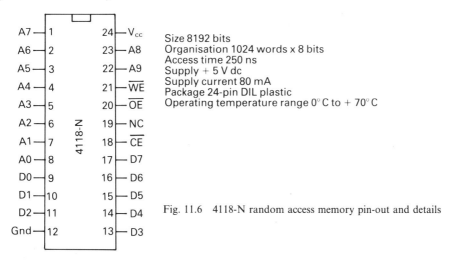

Size 8192 bits
Organisation 1024 words x 8 bits
Access time 250 ns
Supply + 5 V dc
Supply current 80 mA
Package 24-pin DIL plastic
Operating temperature range 0° C to + 70° C

Fig. 11.6   4118-N random access memory pin-out and details

■ An Addressing Circuit

The 4118-N RAM is easy to write to and read from. The processes require the use of several familiar electronic systems, as in Fig. 11.7.

For simple experiments on the logic board, a 4-bit counter can be used to address part of the memory. The counter is connected to the four least significant address pins, A0 to A3. All the other address pins, A4 to A9, are connected to logic 0, 0 V. A hexadecimal display shows which location is

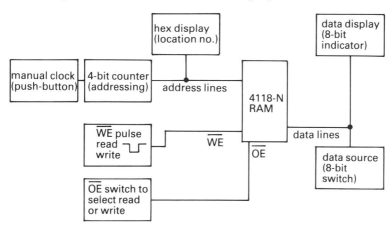

Fig. 11.7   Block diagram of RAM and systems necessary for reading and writing

being addressed. Fig. 11.8 gives the complete circuit for addressing the first 16 lines in the memory.

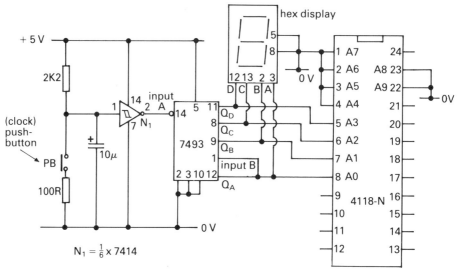

Fig. 11.8   The circuit for addressing the first 16 lines in the memory

■ A Data Input Circuit

The 8-bit switch can supply data to be written into the memory. The switches are connected to the data pins. The 8-bit indicator LEDs are also connected to the data pins, as in Fig. 11.9, to show the binary value of the data.

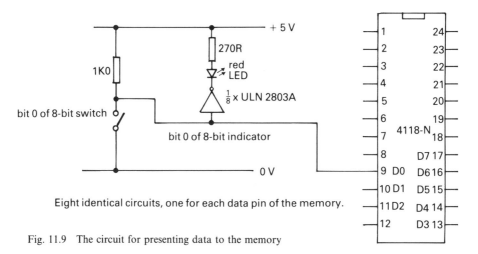

Fig. 11.9   The circuit for presenting data to the memory

Later, if the 8-bit switch is disconnected from the data pins, the 8-bit indicator can display data being read from the memory. If the 8-bit switch is not disconnected, it will continue to present data to the memory. This will be different from the data being read and may damage the integrated circuit.

A Control Circuit

Fig. 11.10 shows the power supply and control connections for the memory. A push-button generates the $\overline{WE}$, write enable, pulse. The push-button does not need to be debounced as the multiple pulses will not cause any problems. Output enable, $\overline{OE}$, can be controlled by the single pole, double throw (SPDT) switch.

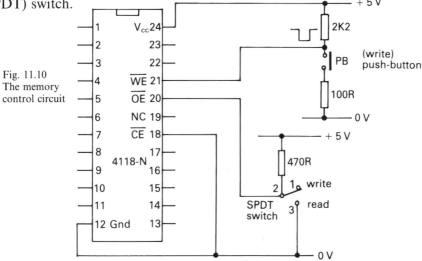

Fig. 11.10
The memory control circuit

Writing and Reading Data — a Practical Test

Any data may be written into the memory, for example, the data given in Table 11.2. First, $\overline{OE}$ must be held at logic 1 by moving the SPDT switch to

Memory location	Data							
	Bit number							
	7	6	5	4	3	2	1	0
0H	0	0	0	0	0	0	0	1
1H	0	0	0	0	0	0	1	0
2H	0	0	0	0	0	1	0	0
3H	0	0	0	0	1	0	0	0
4H	0	0	0	1	0	0	0	0
5H	0	0	1	0	0	0	0	0
6H	0	1	0	0	0	0	0	0
7H	1	0	0	0	0	0	0	0
8H	1	1	0	0	0	0	0	0
9H	0	1	1	0	0	0	0	0
AH	0	0	1	1	0	0	0	0
BH	0	0	0	1	1	0	0	0
CH	0	0	0	0	1	1	0	0
DH	0	0	0	0	0	1	1	0
EH	0	0	0	0	0	0	1	1
FH	1	1	1	1	1	1	1	1

Table 11.2 Data to be written into the memory

the 'write' position. Then the power supply is turned on. The address counter is set to 0H to address the first memory location. The 8-bit switch is set to 0000 0001. These are the data for the first location. The 'write' push-button is pressed once to write the data into the first location. The address counter is incremented to 1H and the process is repeated until all 16 memory locations have data stored in them.

To read data from the memory, the 8-bit switch is disconnected from the data pins. Then, the SPDT switch controlling $\overline{OE}$ is set to 'read'. The address counter is set to the address of the first memory location, 0H. The 8-bit indicator displays the data, 0000 0001, stored in the first location. As the address counter is incremented, the 8-bit indicator displays the data stored in each location. The display agrees with the data listed in Table 11.2.

■ Octal Darlington Driver

The logic board RAM data outputs cannot drive loads, such as LEDs, as they cannot sink or source sufficient current. However, Darlington Driver circuits can overcome this **interfacing** problem. As an 8-bit memory requires eight such circuits, the most convenient way of providing them is by using an octal Darlington Driver integrated circuit, the ULN 2803A, as in Fig. 11.11.

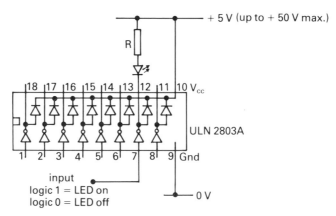

Fig. 11.11   Octal Darlington Driver, ULN 2803A, driving one LED

The inputs of the ULN 2803A octal driver can be connected to any device working on a 5 V power supply. Its outputs can control loads working on the same supply. They can also control loads working on a different supply of up to 50 V. In this case, the 0 V lines of both supplies must be connected.

Each output of the octal driver can sink a current of up to 500 mA. The ULN 2803A outputs each have a reverse biased diode, as in Fig. 11.11 and Fig. 11.12. Additional diodes do not have to be connected across the coils of inductive loads such as relays and solenoids.

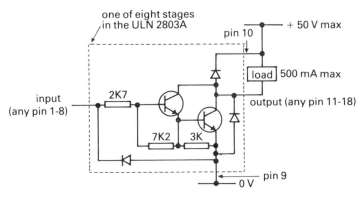

Fig. 11.12   Internal circuit of one stage of the ULN 2803A

The logic board has a ULN 2803A 8-bit buffer at its bottom right-hand corner. Next to it is a +5 V supply socket. This is connected to pin 10 of the integrated circuit if it and its loads are to use the logic board supply.

■   Traffic Lights

The logic board has two sets of red, amber and green LEDs arranged as traffic and pedestrian crossing lights. Each LED is in series with a 270R current-limiting resistor connected to the 5 V rail, as in Fig. 11.13. The LEDs can be controlled by the outputs of the octal buffer. The inputs of the buffer can be controlled by the data outputs of the 4118-N RAM. If the memory is suitably programmed, the traffic lights can be clocked through the familiar colour sequence.

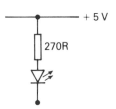

Fig. 11.13   Circuit for one of ten traffic light LEDs

■   Making Connections

The colour sequence for one set of traffic lights is:

> red;
> red and amber;
> green;
> amber;
> red.

Like many others, this sequence repeats continuously. It can be written in circular form, as in Fig. 11.14.

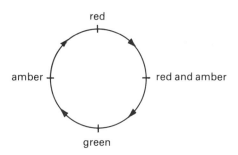

Fig. 11.14   Traffic light sequence in circular form

Each colour must be assigned to a particular output of the 8-bit buffer. Let:

red be controlled by bit 0,
amber be controlled by bit 1,
green be controlled by bit 2.

The corresponding inputs of the 8-bit buffer will be controlled by the corresponding data outputs of the memory, as in Fig. 11.15.

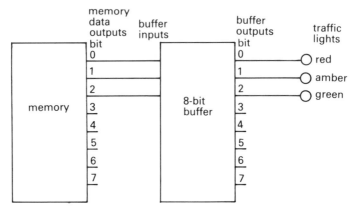

Fig. 11.15 Block diagram of memory, buffer and traffic light connections

■ Work Out the Data

The 8-bit data output from the memory which gives the light sequence is shown in Table 11. 3. Table 11.3 is quite easy to compile. A logic 1 is put in the appropriate place in the table when a light is to be on. A logic 0 is listed if a light is to be off. Table 11.3 lists the data output in hexadecimal as well as binary.

So that the sequence can return from amber (location 3H) back to red (location 0H), the counter which addresses the memory is wired so that it has a maximum count of three.

Memory location	Data output					Green Bit 2	Amber Bit 1	Red Bit 0	Traffic light colour output	Hex equiv. of data output
	Bit 7	Bit 6	Bit 5	Bit 4	Bit 3	Bit 2	Bit 1	Bit 0		
0H	0	0	0	0	0	0	0	1	Red	01H
1H	0	0	0	0	0	0	1	1	Red and amber	03H
2H	0	0	0	0	0	1	0	0	Green	04H
3H	0	0	0	0	0	0	1	0	Amber	02H

Table 11.3 8-bit memory output for the traffic light sequence

■ Different Times

The sequence planned in Table 11.3 makes the traffic lights display each colour for the same length of time. The time depends on the frequency of the clock which is incrementing the address counter. The length of each display is one clock period and is given by the formula:

$$\text{clock period (s)} = 1/\text{clock frequency (Hz)}$$

It is quite easy to make the traffic lights display colours for different lengths of time. It is done by entering the same data in several adjacent memory locations. The result is that, when the memory is being read, it gives the same output for several clock periods.

Let the display time requirement be:

red — 4 clock periods;
red and amber — 1 clock period;
green — 3 clock periods;
amber — 2 clock periods.

The 8-bit data output required from the memory to give the colour sequence and timings is given in Table 11.4.

So that the sequence can return from amber (location 9H) back to red (location 0H), the 4-bit binary counter which addresses the memory must be wired for a maximum count of nine. Alternatively, a decade counter may be used.

Memory location	Data output					Green	Amber	Red	Traffic light colour output	Hex equiv. of data output
	Bit 7	Bit 6	Bit 5	Bit 4	Bit 3	Bit 2	Bit 1	Bit 0		
0H	0	0	0	0	0	0	0	1	Red	01H
1H	0	0	0	0	0	0	0	1		
2H	0	0	0	0	0	0	0	1		
3H	0	0	0	0	0	0	0	1		
4H	0	0	0	0	0	0	1	1	Red and amber	03H
5H	0	0	0	0	0	1	0	0	Green	04H
6H	0	0	0	0	0	1	0	0		
7H	0	0	0	0	0	1	0	0		
8H	0	0	0	0	0	0	1	0	Amber	02H
9H	0	0	0	0	0	0	1	0		

Table 11.4   8-bit memory output for traffic light sequence and timings

☐ Several Traffic Lights — a Worked Example in Memory Programming

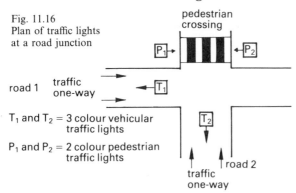

Fig. 11.16
Plan of traffic lights
at a road junction

road 1   traffic
one-way

T_1 and T_2 = 3 colour vehicular
traffic lights

P_1 and P_2 = 2 colour pedestrian
traffic lights

Usually, more than one set of lights is necessary at a road junction so that traffic can be controlled in two directions. At a busy road junction, a complete traffic control system could include pedestrian lights. Fig. 11.16 is the plan of the intersection of two one-way streets. T_1 and T_2 are the traffic lights. P_1 and P_2 are the pedestrian lights.

☐ Software Design

The required sequence of lights is:

1   P_2, P_1 and T_2 all at red while T_1 goes through a complete vehicle sequence from red and back to red;

2   P_2, P_1 and T_1 all at red while T_2 goes through a complete vehicle sequence from red and back to red;

3   T_2 and T_1 both at red while P_1 and P_2 together go through a pedestrian sequence of red to green and back to red.

This outline sequence is expanded in Table 11.5.

Step number	P_2	P_1	T_2	T_1	Comment
1	R	R	R	R	
2	R	R	R	R and A	Road 2 traffic and pedestrians stopped. Traffic flow on road 1.
3	R	R	R	G	
4	R	R	R	A	
5	R	R	R	R	
6	R	R	R and A	R	Road 1 traffic and pedestrians stopped. Traffic flow on road 2.
7	R	R	G	R	
8	R	R	A	R	
9	R	R	R	R	
10	G	G	R	R	Road 1 and road 2 traffic stopped. Pedestrians cross.
	The sequence now repeats.				

Table 11.5   The road junction basic light sequence

138

While Table 11.5 gives the basic light sequence for the road junction, safety requires some display patterns to be maintained for extended periods. Table 11.6 gives the same light sequence as before but with steps 1, 3, 5, 7 and 9 planned so that they are maintained for more than one clock period. The total number of clock periods is 16. This means that a 4-bit binary counter can address a memory which stores the sequence data.

Each colour of the traffic lights T_1, T_2, P_1 and P_2 must be allocated to an output of the 8-bit buffer as in Table 11.7. Each bit will be controlled by the

Step number	P_2	P_1	T_2	T_1	Clock periods	Comment
	R	R	R	R		
1	R	R	R	R	3	
	R	R	R	R		Road 2 traffic and pedestrians stopped. Traffic flow on road 1.
2	R	R	R	R and A	1	
3	R	R	R	G	2	
	R	R	R	G		
4	R	R	R	A	1	
5	R	R	R	R	2	
	R	R	R	R		
6	R	R	R and A	R	1	Road 1 traffic and pedestrians stopped. Traffic flow on road 2.
7	R	R	G	R	2	
	R	R	G	R		
8	R	R	A	R	1	
9	R	R	R	R	2	
	R	R	R	R		
10	G	G	R	R	1	Road 1 and road 2 traffic stopped. Pedestrians cross.
The sequence now repeats.					Total 16	

Table 11.6   The road junction light sequence with varied display timings

P$_1$ and P$_2$		T$_2$			T$_1$		
Green Bit 7	Red Bit 6	Green Bit 5	Amber Bit 4	Red Bit 3	Green Bit 2	Amber Bit 1	Red Bit 0

Table 11.7   Bit allocation of the various traffic light colours

corresponding data output bit of the memory. From Table 11.7, note that the red lights of P$_1$ and P$_2$ are both allocated to bit 6 as they need to be on or off

Step	Memory location	Data output								Comment	Hex equiv. of data output
		P$_1$ and P$_2$		T$_2$			T$_1$				
		Green	Red	Green	Amber	Red	Green	Amber	Red		
		Bit 7	Bit 6	Bit 5	Bit 4	Bit 3	Bit 2	Bit 1	Bit 0		
1	0H	0	1	0	0	1	0	0	1	Road 2 traffic and pedestrians stopped. Traffic flow on road 1.	49H
1	1H	0	1	0	0	1	0	0	1	Road 2 traffic and pedestrians stopped. Traffic flow on road 1.	49H
	2H	0	1	0	0	1	0	0	1		
2	3H	0	1	0	0	1	0	1	1		4BH
3	4H	0	1	0	0	1	1	0	0		4CH
3	5H	0	1	0	0	1	1	0	0		4CH
4	6H	0	1	0	0	1	0	1	0		4AH
5	7H	0	1	0	0	1	0	0	1		49H
5	8H	0	1	0	0	1	0	0	1		49H
6	9H	0	1	0	1	1	0	0	1	Road 1 traffic and pedestrians stopped. Traffic flow on road 2.	59H
7	AH	0	1	1	0	0	0	0	1	Road 1 traffic and pedestrians stopped. Traffic flow on road 2.	61H
7	BH	0	1	1	0	0	0	0	1		61H
8	CH	0	1	0	1	0	0	0	1		51H
9	DH	0	1	0	0	1	0	0	1		49H
9	EH	0	1	0	0	1	0	0	1		49H
10	FH	1	0	0	0	1	0	0	1	Roads 1 and 2 traffic stopped. Pedestrians cross.	89H

Table 11.8   8-bit memory output for the traffic light sequence and timings

together. The green lights of P_1 and P_2 are both allocated to bit 7 for the same reason.

Table 11.8 is Table 11.6 rewritten to show the data which have to be stored in each of the 16 memory locations which control the traffic lights.

☐ Hardware Design

The data preparation process just described is a **software design process**. The data are the software. The **hardware** is the equipment which will store the data and control the traffic lights.

The design of hardware is best tackled in two stages. First, draw a block diagram to identify the essential parts of the system, as in Fig. 11.17. Second, design a circuit for each of the essential parts.

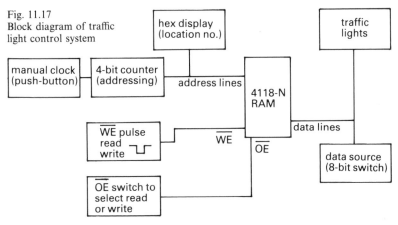

Fig. 11.17
Block diagram of traffic light control system

The memory addressing circuit can be as shown in Fig. 11.8. The memory control circuit can be as shown in Fig. 11.10. The circuit for presenting data to the memory can be as shown in Fig. 11.18.

Fig. 11.18   The circuit for presenting data to the memory

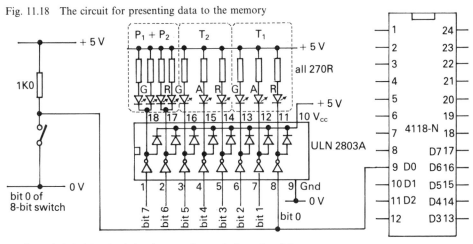

One of eight identical circuits, one for each data pin of the memory.

The circuit shown in Fig. 11.18 allows each data entry to be checked against the traffic light display before it is written into the memory. Once the memory is programmed, the 8-bit switch must be disconnected before the system begins to sequence the lights.

A 1 Hz clock can be used to run the system automatically. The clock is connected to pin 14 of the 4-bit binary counter in place of the push-button and its debouncing circuit shown in Fig. 11.8.

While this system is based on a memory chip, other hardware could be used and it need not be electronic. The hardware could be electro-mechanical. A central heating clock is an example of an electro-mechanical sequencing device. The hardware could be purely mechanical. A musical box is an example of a mechanical sequencing device. Whatever the hardware, the software is the same. It is like some lines of music. It describes what is to happen and not how it is to be made to happen.

☐ **Some Ideas For Memories**

Fig. 11.19 outlines a circuit which will make a sequence run only once after a push-button has been pressed. Unless input E of the AND gate is at logic 1, pulses from the system clock cannot reach the counter which addresses the memory. Input E is controlled by output C of the OR gate.

The memory is programmed so that the most significant bit (MSB), bit 7, is always at logic 1 except in the first location of the memory. Here it is at logic 0.

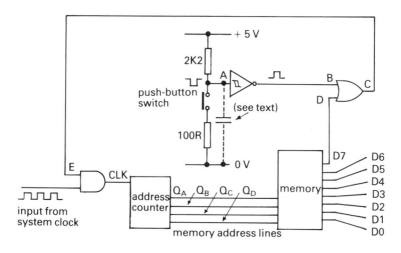

Fig. 11.19
Outline circuit to allow a memory sequence to run once only

When the system is waiting to operate, the memory is addressed at location 0H. Inputs B and D of the OR gate are at logic 0. Therefore output C of the OR gate is at logic 0 and so is input E of the AND gate. The address counter cannot increment as clock pulses cannot reach it.

When the push-button is pressed, input A of the inverter goes to logic 0.

142

This gives logic 1 at B. In turn, this gives logic 1 at C and E. This allows a clock pulse to increment the memory address from 0H to 1H. The memory now outputs a logic 1 from bit 7. This gives logic 1 at D, C and E. The result is that clock pulses can continue to increment the address counter until the counter returns to zero. At this address, bit 7 outputs logic 0 again. This causes logic 0 at input E. This stops clock pulses reaching the address counter and so the sequence halts.

If the clock period is long and the time for which the push-button is pressed is short, the sequence will not always trigger into action. Input A should be at logic 0 for just longer than the clock period. The time for which input A is at logic 0 can be controlled by a large capacitor, up to 2500μ. It is connected between input A and the 0 V line as in Fig. 11.19. However, this solution is satisfactory only where the times involved are just a few seconds long.

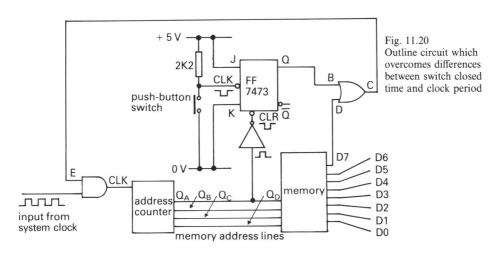

Fig. 11.20 Outline circuit which overcomes differences between switch closed time and clock period

Fig. 11.20 shows a better way of overcoming the timing problem. The 7473 flip-flop allows any time difference to be accommodated with complete reliability. With the flip-flop J input at logic 1 and the K input at logic 0, closure of the switch causes Q to go to logic 1. This gives logic 1 at B, C and E and allows the system clock pulses to reach the counter so that it can increment. Output Q_A of the counter is inverted and used to give a CLEAR (CLR) signal to the flip-flop. This causes Q to return to logic 0. This ensures that memory addressing will cease when the counter returns to zero. For a more detailed understanding of Fig. 11.20, revise the 7473 flip-flop and the 4-bit binary counter.

A 'once through' system could control the lights at a Pelican crossing or it might be used in a coin-in-the-slot machine.

In practical circuits, a RAM such as the 4118-N is useful when work is at an experimental stage and the software is not finalised. When the design is complete, the software can be stored in an EPROM so that it is not lost every time the power supply is turned off. A 2716 or 2516 EPROM is suitable but, beware, there are two versions of these integrated circuits. One version requires a +5 V power supply for normal operation while the other requires +5 V and −5 V and +12 V supplies. The version easiest to use is the one which requires the single 5 V supply. Do not confuse the normal operating power supply requirements with the 25 V supply both versions require when data are being written into them.

The 2716/2516 EPROM is organised as 2048 words × 8 bits. It has twice the number of locations of the 4118-N. A special circuit called an **EPROM programmer** is used to write the data into the memory. Professional EPROM programmers are expensive but designs for amateur programmers are published from time to time in electronics magazines. Some designs are 'stand alone' units. Others are add-on units for popular personal microcomputers. A design for the latter type is included in the Teacher's Guide to this book. Both types of programmer are inexpensive and easy to build and use.

If a 4118-N RAM is used for development work and an EPROM used in the final product, you must allow for differences in the pin designations of the two memories.

12 The Microprocessor

■ The Microcomputer

Inside the case of a **microcomputer** such as the BBC and Spectrum machines, you will see a number of interconnected digital integrated circuits. Many of them are identical in function to those studied in this book. The most important of these integrated circuits is one called a **microprocessor**.

■ The Microprocessor

There are many different microprocessors. Each has an identifying number. The **Z80 microprocessor** is used in very many different microcomputers including the Spectrum and Amstrad machines. The **6502 microprocessor** is used much less widely and is found in the BBC microcomputer. The Z80 and the 6502 are not identical, but they work in similar ways and do similar things. They cost only a few pounds in electronic component shops.

Internally, a microprocessor is a complex electronic circuit. Externally, it looks like a large version of the integrated circuits on the logic board. The Z80 and 6502 both have 40 pins. Just as on a memory chip, there are data pins, address pins and control pins.

A microprocessor is no use on its own. It is a bit like a brain without a body. It needs to be connected to other chips to form a working system, i.e. a microcomputer. In this chapter, we shall look at the essential parts of a microcomputer, how they are linked together and what they do.

■ Instructions

A microprocessor is a device which obeys **instructions**.

Fig. 12.1 is a list of instructions which may seem familiar!
Mum's list is a memory system. Instructions have been stored as graphite squiggles on paper. When she is ready, Jean will read the list and carry out each instruction in turn.

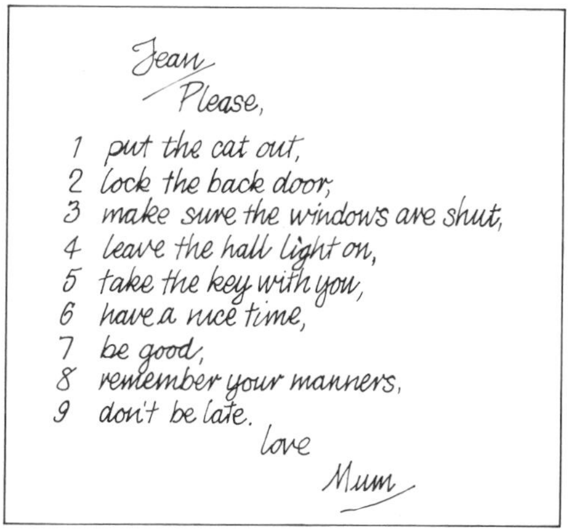

> Jean
> Please,
> 1 put the cat out,
> 2 lock the back door,
> 3 make sure the windows are shut,
> 4 leave the hall light on,
> 5 take the key with you,
> 6 have a nice time,
> 7 be good,
> 8 remember your manners,
> 9 don't be late.
> love
> Mum

Fig. 12.1   A list of instructions

In a similar way, a memory integrated circuit stores instructions for a microprocessor to obey. The instructions are in the form of a list of binary numbers written into the memory locations. When it is ready, the microprocessor reads the instructions from the memory and obeys them one at a time.

■ Buses

The memory and the microprocessor are connected together, data pins to data pins, address pins to address pins. Only some of the control pins on the microprocessor connect to the control pins on the memory. Each of the three groups of connections is called a **bus**, as in Fig.12.2.

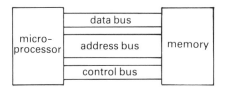

Fig. 12.2   A microprocessor and a memory connected

The Z80 and 6502 microprocessors have eight data pins, D0 to D7. The 8-bit **data bus** allows the microprocessor to read instructions in the memory. Both microprocessors have a 16-bit **program counter**. Its output is at the address pins, A0 to A15. The program counter addresses the memory locations by way of the **address bus**. The **control bus** allows the microprocessor and the rest of the system to tell each other when they are ready for something to happen.

■ There's More to an Instruction than Meets the Eye

When Jean reads her Mum's list, as in Fig. 12.1, she knows what each instruction means and how to obey it. This ability has been 'built into' her by various means. For example, she knows that 'put the cat out' means:

1   find the cat;
2   drag it out from its hiding place;
3   avoid being scratched;
4   carry the cat down stairs;
5   open the back door;
6   push the cat through the doorway into the garden;
7   shut the back door quickly.

It can take some time to do all of this.

Similarly, a microprocessor knows what to do once it has read an instruction. This ability was built into it when it was manufactured. When obeying an instruction, a microprocessor has to make many checks and decisions before it completes the task. Again, this takes time.

146

One Thing at a Time

Jean has to work through the checks and decisions of each instruction in an orderly, 'one-thing-at-a-time' manner. A microprocessor works in the same way. To enable this to happen, a **clock** is connected to the microprocessor, as in Fig. 12.3. Each clock pulse makes the microprocessor complete a step of an instruction. The clock runs at several megahertz.

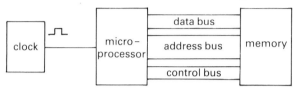

Fig. 12.3 A microprocessor system with its clock

Instruction Set

A big difference between Jean and a microprocessor is the number of instructions each is able to obey. Who knows how many instructions a human being could obey? We know for certain that a Z80 microprocessor has only 158 instructions to which it can respond. As microchips go, that is quite a lot.

The list of instructions a microprocessor can obey is called its **instruction set**. Each instruction is numbered. When a user wants the microprocessor to perform a particular task, the appropriate instructions from the instruction set are selected and a list made of their numbers. It is rather like selecting a meal from a Chinese menu. This process is called **writing a program**. When the program is finalised, the numbers are written into the memory connected to the microprocessor. The numbers are, of course, 8-bit binary numbers.

Example
The user wants the microprocessor to obey the instruction 'Halt'. For the Z80 microprocessor, the binary code number for 'Halt' is 0111 0110. This number is written into a memory location. Later, when the microprocessor reads this location, it obeys the 'Halt' instruction. The instruction means just what it says. The microprocessor stops work. It 'goes to sleep' until the user 'wakes it up' with a reset signal.

An Answer is Required

Fig. 12.4 shows a set of instructions written by Jean for Alan. Part of Alan's task is to write an answer in a box.

Alan,

Work out 2+2 and then write your answer in this box ⟶ ☐

Jean

Fig. 12.4   Instructions which require a reply

In much the same way, a microprocessor can be asked to add 2 and 2 and write the answer in a memory location. The memory in the microcomputer, as in Fig. 12.5, has to be random access memory (RAM) so that the microprocessor can write answers to it as well as read instructions from it.

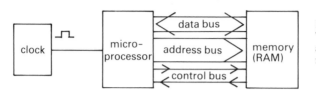

Fig. 12.5
The direction of flow along the buses of a microprocessor system

■ More About Buses

Because data pass in either direction, the data bus is called a **bidirectional bus**. The arrows in Fig. 12.5 indicate this. As will be seen later, data can pass along the bus to and from devices other than memory chips.

The control bus is also bidirectional but, unlike the data bus, it uses one set of connections for control signals to the microprocessor and another set of connections for control signals from the microprocessor. Some control bus signals tell the memory if the microprocessor wants to read from it or write to it.

The address bus is a **unidirectional bus**. Through it, the microprocessor's 16-bit program counter addresses memory locations and other parts of the system. The counter does not increment with every clock pulse. It increments only after an instruction has been read from the memory. The following clock pulses cause each step of an instruction to be completed. Only then is the next instruction read and the program counter incremented again.

■ Decisions

In following her Mum's instructions, as in Fig.12.6, Jean obeys instruction 1. When she comes to instruction 2, she has to make a decision. She checks

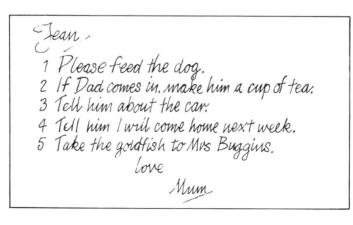

Fig. 12.6
Another list of instructions

whether or not her Dad is in. If he is not in, she misses out the rest of instruction 2 and instructions 3 and 4 and gets on with instruction 5. Her 'program counter' has produced an 'address output' of 1, 2, 5. If her Dad had been in, her 'program counter' would have produced an 'address output' of 1, 2, 3, 4, 5.

Many programs require a microprocessor to make decisions about what instruction to obey next. The microprocessor is able to alter its program counter to fit in with its decision.

■ **Dictation**

Earlier in this chapter, we saw in Fig. 12.1 and Fig. 12.6 two lists of instructions from Mum to Jean. What we did not know was that, earlier in the day, Mum dictated these instructions and Jean wrote them down. Jean learned how to listen and write at primary school. The knowledge is stored in part of her brain. The brain cells form a read only memory, ROM. When Jean had to write the lists, she let the 'program' stored in that part of her brain control her. Fig.12.7 is a block diagram which summarises the process.

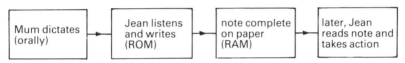

Fig. 12.7   Note writing — dictation to action

When we want a microprocessor to do a job for us, we dictate our requirements to it. We cannot dictate orally, although this is possible in some very advanced systems! We have to do it in a very laborious manner: we operate switches on a keyboard with our fingers.

■ **System Monitor**

The microprocessor is connected to a read only memory, ROM. It stores a program called the **system monitor**. This tells the microprocessor how to 'listen' to our switch-dictated instructions and write them into the random access memory, RAM. Later, the microprocessor addresses the RAM, reads our instructions and obeys them. Fig. 12.8 is a block diagram which summarises this process.

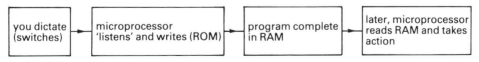

Fig. 12.8   Programming the computer — 'dictation' to action

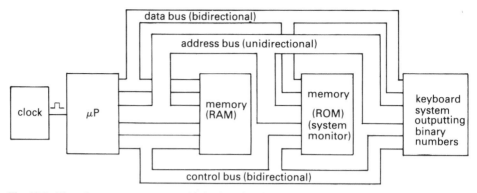

Fig. 12.9 The microprocessor system with keyboard and ROM added

Fig. 12.9 shows the original system of clock, microprocessor and RAM, as shown in Fig. 12.5, with a keyboard and ROM added.

■ Hexadecimal Keyboards

People dictated programs to the first computers by setting 8-bit binary numbers on 8-bit switches. We used a similar method when programming a RAM in Activity 11. The snag with this method is that it is very slow and tedious and, worse still, it is very easy to make mistakes.

The task is made easier if the 8-bit switch is replaced by a **hexadecimal keyboard**. The hexadecimal numbers are easier to read, understand and check than binary numbers. Each key is a push-button switch. If a key is pressed, the microprocessor is presented with the binary equivalent of the hexadecimal number written on the key. The microprocessor, instructed by the ROM, immediately writes the number into the RAM.

Example

The binary code number for the 'Halt' instruction is 0111 0110. The hexadecimal equivalent of 0111 0110 is &76. If the 'Halt' instruction is required, we press key '7' and then key '6'. The microprocessor is presented with 0111 0110 which it writes into the RAM.

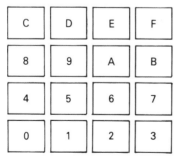

The keyboard needs some electronic hardware to link it to the data, address and control buses. The details need not concern us now. Fig. 12.10 shows the layout of a typical hexadecimal keyboard.

Fig. 12.10 Hexadecimal keyboard layout

■ Machine Code

When hexadecimal numbers are keyed into a microprocessor system, we say it is being programmed in **machine code**. When a microprocessor obeys a

150

machine code program, it does so in the shortest possible time. This high-speed operation is very important in critical situations such as aircraft navigation and control. It is also essential for good, fast-moving graphics displays in computer games.

■ QWERTY Keyboards

Although a hexadecimal keyboard is much more convenient and accurate than an 8-bit switch, the drawback is that the code for each instruction has to be looked up in a book. Also, the programmer has to have a very detailed knowledge of the microprocessor. It would be more convenient if we could dictate our instructions in English. For example, if the 'Halt' instruction was required, H A L T would be entered on a keyboard just like typing on a typewriter.

The keyboard needed is an **alpha-numeric keyboard**. It requires at least 36 push-button keyswitches, 26 for the letters of the alphabet and ten for the digits 0 to 9. These keyboards are also called **QWERTY keyboards** because the left-hand end of the top row of the alphabet keys spells 'QWERTY', as in Fig. 12.11. Electronic circuits connect the keyboard to the buses.

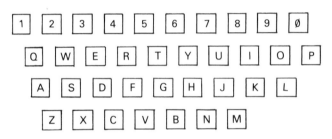

Fig. 12.11   QWERTY keyboard layout (note the manner in which the letter O and the digit 0 are frequently distinguished)

□ ASCII Code

If H A L T is typed on the keyboard, the microprocessor is presented with four binary numbers which represent those letters and not the binary code for the 'Halt' instruction. There is an international standard binary code for the letters of the alphabet and the digits 0 to 9. It is the **American Standard Code for Information Interchange**, the **ASCII** (pronounced 'Askey') **code**. It is the ASCII codes for the letters and digits which the microprocessor writes into the RAM at our 'dictation'.

When a microprocessor obeys a program dictated in English, it takes quite a long time to complete the task. This is because it has to sort through the ASCII code to discover the instructions it is to obey. The process of sorting is a work of translation. It is done by an **interpreter program** also stored in the ROM. Usually, the time penalty is outweighed by the convenience of being able to program in English.

■ High-level Languages

The 'English' must conform to very strict rules if the microprocessor is to understand our dictation. This type of English is called a **high-level programming language**. BASIC is a very widely used example of such a language. BASIC is short for **Beginners All-purpose Symbolic Instruction Code**.

A high-level language requires the microprocessor system to have a large amount of RAM. This is because programs are very long when compared with the same program written in machine code. The popular personal microcomputers are advertised as being, for example, 32K or 48K or 128K machines. These figures refer to the amount of RAM they have and it governs the length of the programs that the microcomputer can handle.

There are other high-level languages, e.g. Forth, Pascal, Cobol and Logo. Each has its own strict rules and is best suited to a particular purpose. High-level languages are said to be **user-friendly** because they enable us to 'dictate' to a microprocessor with minimal difficulty.

□ Assembly Language

Between machine code and high-level languages is **assembly language**. The programmer uses a QWERTY keyboard and types abbreviations of the commands in the microprocessor instruction set, e.g. LD for load, DEC for decrement, JP for jump. These abbreviations are called **mnemonics**. If, for example, 'DEC' is typed on the keyboard, the microprocessor writes into the RAM the binary code number for that instruction, 0011 1101. This is the same as what happens when the microcomputer is programmed in machine code. When the microprocessor obeys instructions entered in assembly language, it does so at machine code speed. Machine code and assembly language are called **low-level languages**.

■ Talk to Me

Communication needs to be two-way. The microprocessor must be able to tell us what it has worked out, for example, that two plus two is four. It is also very useful if the microprocessor repeats back to us each instruction as we dictate it. Advanced systems do have a voice. More usually the microprocessor talks to us in a visual way, for example, by printing something on paper or on a calculator-type display or on a television screen.

A small calculator-type display can show us, in hexadecimal, the address of a memory location and the data stored in it, as in Table 12.1. When programming in machine code, this type of display is quite adequate and has the advantages of being reliable, cheap, light in weight and compact.

Memory location	Location contents
0800	3E

Table 12.1 A simple calculator-type display for a microprocessor system

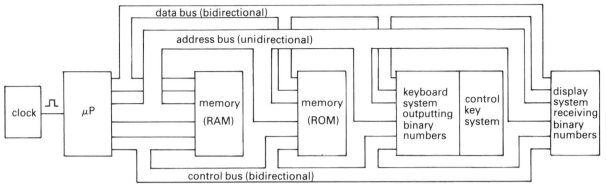

Fig. 12.12   Microprocessor system with display and control key systems added

The system monitor program stored in the ROM tells the microprocessor how to 'talk' back to us through whatever display system is being used. Some electronic circuitry is necessary to make the display system work. This circuitry is connected to the data, address and control buses of the microprocessor as in Fig. 12.12.

■ Control Keys

In addition to the programming keys, some control keys are necessary. For a small machine code microcomputer, two keys are essential. One could be marked RUN. When this key is pressed, the microprocessor begins to obey the instructions stored in the RAM. The other could be marked RESET. When pressed, this key stops the microprocessor obeying our instructions and makes it ready to write a new program into the RAM at our dictation.

Two more keys would be very useful. They could be marked UP and DOWN. They would allow us to move up and down the memory so that we could see, on a calculator-type display, the contents of each location. Fig. 12.13 shows a control keyboard layout. Some integrated circuits link the control keyboard to the data, address and control buses, as in Fig. 12.12.

The control keys for a microcomputer with a QWERTY keyboard may have names different from those suggested for a machine code microcomputer. You could spend a few moments identifying the control keys on a Spectrum or BBC microcomputer.

Fig. 12.13   A control keyboard layout for a machine code microprocessor system

□ Memory Map

When the RAM is being programmed, the microprocessor is working with the ROM. When programming is complete, the microprocessor works with the RAM and obeys the programmer's instructions. The memory locations in the ROM and the RAM must have different addresses. A **memory map** is a diagram that shows which addresses are allocated to each memory.

153

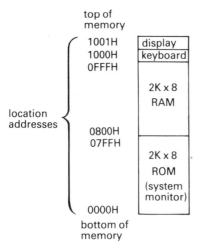

top of
memory

location
addresses

1001H	display
1000H	keyboard
0FFFH	
	2K x 8 RAM
0800H	
07FFH	
	2K x 8 ROM (system monitor)
0000H	

bottom of
memory

Fig. 12.14   Memory map for a small
microprocessor system

Fig. 12.14 is the memory map of a small microprocessor system. The ROM is a 2K memory, i.e. 2048 words of eight bits each. It is allocated to addresses from 0000H to 07FFH (07FFH is 2047 in decimal). The RAM is also a 2K memory of 2048 words of eight bits each. It is allocated to addresses from 0800F to 0FFFH. When a program is being 'dictated' through the keyboard, the microprocessor writes it into the RAM starting at location 0800H and continues through addresses 0801H, 0802H and so on. An 8-bit binary number is stored at each location.

Address &0000 is called the **bottom of the memory**. Many people draw memory maps with that address at the bottom, as in Fig. 12.14.

The name 'memory map' is a little misleading. **Address map** would be better. This is because the ROM and the RAM are not the only devices with which a microprocessor deals in binary numbers via the data bus. It also reads numbers from the keyboard and it writes numbers to the display. The keyboard and display have to have their own unique addresses, e.g. 1000H and 1001H, so that communication takes place with the right device at the right time. These addresses are included in the memory map in Fig. 12.14.

■ Peripherals

While the microprocessor is obeying our instructions stored in the RAM, it may need information from us and it may give us information.

We can give the microprocessor information through the keyboard. This is what happens in games programs. Keys on which English words were typed when programming now move objects, control space ships and fire rockets.

The display, which let us see what we were telling the microprocessor when we were programming, can be used by the microprocessor to give us information by, for example, showing us where it has moved our space ship.

When the keyboard and display are used in this way, the keyboard is an **input device** and the display is an **output device**. Input and output devices are known as **peripherals**. Among other peripherals are a **joystick** (input), a **digitiser** (input), a **printer** (output) and an **X-Y plotter** (output). A peripheral must have its own address so that it can send or receive the right data at the right time.

■ Controlling Machines

A microprocessor system can be used as a machine controller. The machine might be a space shuttle or a car engine, a domestic washing machine or a sewing machine, a coal mine, a robot in a factory or a life-support machine in a hospital. These systems still require a keyboard and display. But when the program is running, the microprocessor needs to acquire information from the machine being controlled and it needs to give information to the machine.

Sensors can gather information for a microprocessor. The sensors can include mechanical switches, light-dependent resistors and thermistors. The circuits for these devices are discussed earlier in this book.

The microprocessor can control a machine through Darlington Driver circuits. These might control relays which, in turn, control motors, lamps, solenoids and audible alarms.

■ Input-output Interface

Information from the sensors passes to the microprocessor along the data bus. Information from the microprocessor to the Darlington Drivers passes back along the data bus. An **input-output interface** does the very important job of connecting the sensors and the Darlington Drivers to the data bus whenever the microprocessor wants to receive or send information.

Fig. 12.15 is a block diagram of a microprocessor system arranged to control a machine.

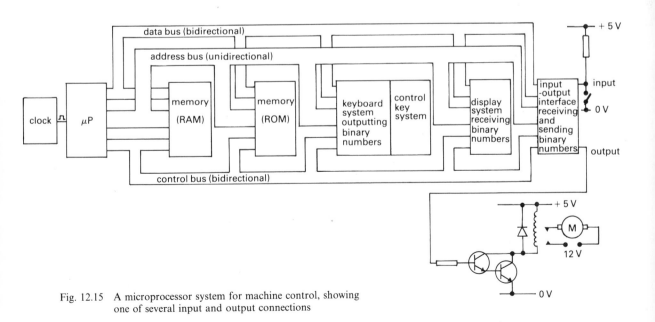

Fig. 12.15   A microprocessor system for machine control, showing
one of several input and output connections

155

■ Input-output Ports

The input-output interface is connected to the data, address and control buses as in Fig. 12.16. It has its own address in the memory map. It is another device from which the microprocessor can read an 8-bit binary number or to which it can write an 8-bit binary number.

The eight lines D0 to D7, to which sensors can be connected, are called the **input port**. Each line is a logic gate input. Therefore a sensor must hold a line at logic 0 or logic 1.

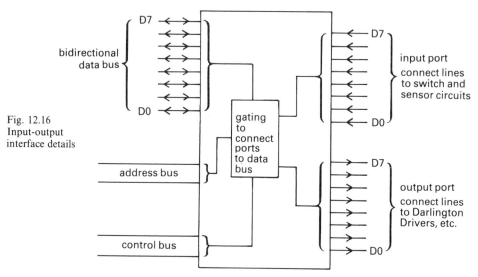

Fig. 12.16
Input-output
interface details

In a small control system, only one line might be used, say, D0. The microprocessor always reads all eight lines because it expects an 8-bit binary number on its data bus. Therefore, the unused lines, D1 to D7, must be connected to a logic level, say, logic 0. If D0 is at logic 0, the microprocessor sees the 8-bit binary number 0000 0000 when it reads the input port. If D0 is at logic 1, the microprocessor sees 0000 0001 when it reads the port.

The eight lines D0 to D7, to which Darlington Drivers can be connected, are called the **output port**. The microprocessor can switch a line to logic 0 or logic 1.

In a small system, only one line might be used, say D0. But, the microprocessor always writes an 8-bit binary number to the port. Therefore, if D0 is to be at logic 0, the microprocessor writes 0000 0000 to the port. If D0 is to be at logic 1, the microprocessor writes 0000 0001 to the port.

Logic gates in the interface receive signals from the address and control buses to connect the input or output port to the data bus at the right moment for reading or writing.

■ Interpack and Intercard

The Spectrum and BBC microcomputers can be machine controllers if they are fitted with an input-output interface. There are many of these on the market.

Activities 12 and 13 in the Workbooks introduce ideas used in the control of machines. They are written for the Spectrum and BBC computers. It is assumed that a Spectrum is connected to an **Interpack Interface** fitted with a **Spectrum Intercard** and that a BBC is connected to an **Interpack Interface** fitted with a **BBC Intercard**.

These interfaces are versatile devices. They have an 8-bit input port and an 8-bit output port. These ports are used in Activities 12 and 13. In addition, they have other features not used in Activities 12 and 13, namely:

1   four outputs direct from the contacts of four relays. The relays are the same as the one on the logic board.

2   four inputs to which switches can be connected. No pull-up resistors are needed.

3   an 8-channel, 8-bit **analogue to digital (A to D) converter**. This is an input. It allows the computer to read up to eight different sensors responding to physical changes. For example, the computer could take regular readings of a slowly changing temperature sensed by a thermistor and make a note of them.

4   an expansion connector which allows other units to be connected to the interface.

These additional features are described in the interface leaflet. Also, there are programs and ideas for tests and experiments available from Griffin and George Limited.

■ Addresses

The Spectrum Interpack 8-bit input and output ports have the same address, 95. This is a decimal number.

The BBC Interpack 8-bit input and output ports have the same address, &FCC2.

Other details in a computer program decide if the microprocessor is to read (input) from the address or write (output) to the address.

■ Computer Health Warning

Please take great care to protect computers and their accessories from accidental electrical damage. Mistakes can be very expensive!

Connect an input-output interface to a computer only when all power supplies are switched off.

Disconnect an input-output interface from a computer only when all power supplies are switched off.

Make and break connections between an input-output interface and the logic board or other systems only when all power supplies are switched off.

Always assume you have made a mistake. Therefore, always double-check that all connections are correct before switching on any power supplies. Take your time. Do not rush.

■ Connections

The input and output ports on the Interpacks are available at 10-way Molex sockets. Each socket has '1' moulded at its left-hand end and '10' moulded at its right-hand end.

Pin 1 on the sockets is the 0 V rail of the computer power supply. A pin 1 (it does not matter which) must always be connected to the logic board 0 V rail.

Pin 10 on the sockets is the $+5$ V rail of the computer power supply. This must *not* be connected to the logic board.

Pins 2 to 9 are the 8-bit ports proper and are D0 to D7 of the computer's data bus. Take care: D0 has been put on the left!

An adaptor is needed to connect the Molex sockets to the 2 mm sockets on the logic board.

Each line of the output port is the output of a logic gate. Each can sink a maximum current of 15 mA. A line can drive the input of another logic gate. The port can drive the logic board 8-bit indicator directly. Any other devices should be driven through a Darlington Driver. Not all of the lines need be used. Lines not required are left unconnected.

Each line of the input port is the input of a logic gate. The port may be connected directly to the 8-bit switch. Input lines may also be controlled by any of the switch or sensor circuits explored in earlier chapters and activities. If not all of the input lines are required, the unused lines *must* be held at a logic level. Logic 0 is the most convenient.

■ At Power-up

When connections have been made and double-checked, the computer and logic board power supplies can be switched on. At power-up, the output port will always have a garbage mixture of logic 0s and 1s. Also, some of the relay coils in the interface may energise. The port must be reset and the relay coils switched off before anything else is done. Key these instructions into the computer:

Spectrum
OUT 95,0 followed by ENTER   (resets all output lines to logic 0)
OUT 63,0 followed by ENTER   (de-energises relay coils)

BBC
?&FCC2 = 0 followed by RETURN   (resets all output lines to logic 0)
?&FCC1 = 0 followed by RETURN   (de-energises relay coils)

Perform this routine every time the system is powered.

■ Output an 8-bit Binary Number

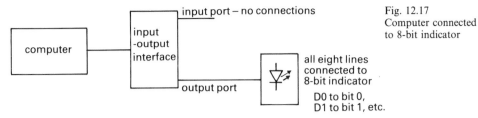

input port – no connections

Fig. 12.17
Computer connected
to 8-bit indicator

all eight lines
connected to
8-bit indicator
D0 to bit 0,
D1 to bit 1, etc.

Fig. 12.17 is a block diagram of a computer connected to the logic board 8-bit indicator by the input-output interface. We can tell the computer to make the indicator display an 8-bit binary number between 0000 0000 and 1111 1111 (0 and 255 in decimal, 00 and FF in hex). The number can be given to the Spectrum in either decimal or binary. It can be given to the BBC computer in either decimal or hexadecimal as in Fig. 12.18.

Fig. 12.18   Output instructions

       OUT 95,BIN 11111111 (followed by ENTER)
  or OUT 95,255 (followed by ENTER)

  a) Spectrum instructions (BIN is an E-mode keyword on the B key)

       ?&FCC2 = 255 (followed by RETURN)
  or ?&FCC2 = &FF (followed by RETURN)

  b) BBC instructions (the & sign tells the computer that FF is a hex number, not two letters)

If these instructions are keyed into the computer, all of the LEDs illuminate. If different numbers are keyed in, the display changes to agree with them.

■   Programs

Rather than give **direct commands**, as in Fig. 12.18, we usually incorporate our instructions in a **program**. All of the programs in Activity 12 are written in BASIC. Each assignment is in two versions, Spectrum BASIC and BBC BASIC and are as near identical as possible.

Fig. 12.19 shows a short BASIC program. It tells the computer to output a number to the 8-bit indicator. Because we can vary the number from 0 to 255, it is called a **variable**. In the program we let a symbol, x, stand for this variable number.

Fig. 12.19
Program to output
a number to the
8-bit indicator

10 LET x = BIN 11111111	10 LET X = &FF
20 OUT 95,x	20 ?&FCC2 = X
30 STOP	30 STOP
a) Spectrum BASIC	b) BBC BASIC

In line 10 of the program, we tell the computer that the value of x is to be binary 1111 1111 or &FF (in both cases we could have used 255). In line 20

159

we tell the computer to output the value of x to the 8-bit indicator. When the program is run, all the LEDs will illuminate. Line 30 tells the computer that the task is completed.

Our instructions are carried out when we key in RUN. The program can be edited and the value of x, line 10, can be altered.

All control programs are about getting a value for the variable x, and outputting it.

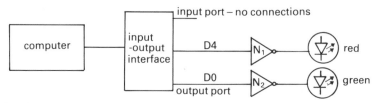

Fig. 12.20   Output port controls two LEDs connected to lines D0 and D4

$N_1 = N_2 =$ Darlington Driver

Fig. 12.20 shows the output port controlling two LEDs connected to lines D0 and D4 by Darlington Drivers. Table 12.2 lists all combinations of light output and the binary values of x which give them.

Red	Green	Binary value of x							
D4	D0	D7	D6	D5	D4	D3	D2	D1	D0
Off	Off	0	0	0	0	0	0	0	0
Off	On	0	0	0	0	0	0	0	1
On	Off	0	0	0	1	0	0	0	0
On	On	0	0	0	1	0	0	0	1

Table 12.2   Light output and value of x

■ Input an 8-bit Binary Number

Fig. 12.21 shows a computer connected by the input-output interface ports to the 8-bit switch and the 8-bit indicator. A binary number at the input port is set on the 8-bit switch. The computer is to be asked to read the number and then output it to the 8-bit indicator display. The number is another variable as it can be anything from 0000 0000 to 1111 1111. Let the number be called x.

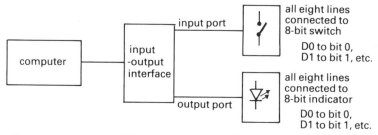

Fig. 12.21   Computer connected to 8-bit switch and 8-bit indicator

160

Fig. 12.22 is the program for this task. Line 10 tells the computer to read the value of x at the input port. Line 20 tells the computer to write the value of x to the output port. Line 30 tells the computer that it has completed the task.

Fig. 12.22
Program to read a
binary number from
the 8-bit switch and
output it to the 8-bit
indicator

10 LET x = IN 95	10 X = ?&FCC2
20 OUT 95,x	20 ?&FCC2 = X
30 STOP	30 STOP
a) Spectrum BASIC	b) BBC BASIC

All control signals from a machine are read into a computer in this way. The signals may come from switch or sensor circuits. In complex systems, a computer may spend some time processing what it has read before it produces an output. The output is not usually identical to the input as in this example.

■ Summary

Fig. 12.23 summarises a microprocessor system, a computer, working as a controller. At its simplest, you can think of it as two systems which have the microprocessor, ROM and RAM in common.

System one takes the orders for system two. In system one, the microprocessor and ROM work together to receive a program through the keyboard and store it in RAM. The microprocessor and the ROM also work together to display the program details.

In system two, the microprocessor and the RAM work with the input and output ports to control a machine or process.

Fig. 12.23   The microprocessor system

161

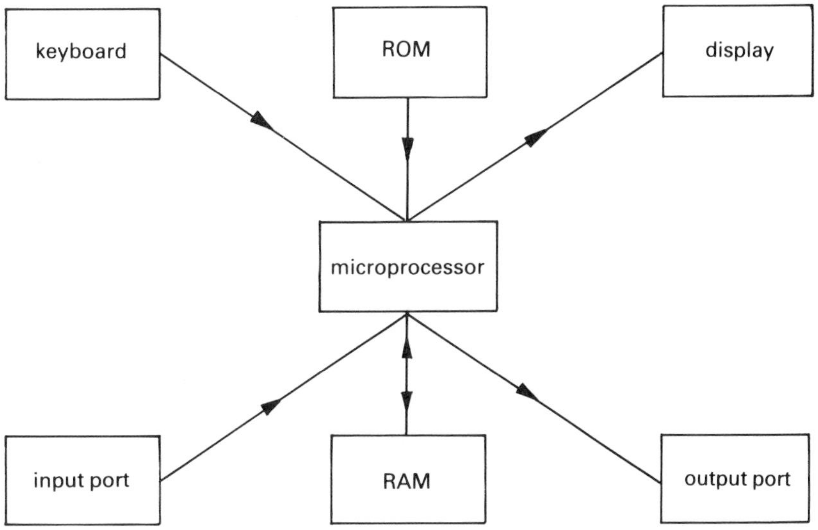

13 Machine Code Programming

When using a high-level language such as BASIC, a programmer need know nothing about a microprocessor or any other component in a computer. The computer will work for the user as long as all the rules of the language are obeyed.

By contrast, **machine code programmming** requires a good knowledge of the **microprocessor**, its **instruction set** and the **address map** of the computer.

☐ Registers

A bicycle has many parts — such as the frame, the wheels, the pedals and the saddle. A rider is interested in what these parts do, not how they do it. A microprocessor, too, has many parts. A machine code programmer must know what they do but need not bother with how they do it. We shall concentrate on just one group of parts, the **registers**.

All microprocessors have registers. They are rather like memory locations. Each can store a binary number. Some microprocessors have registers which store 1-bit binary numbers while others have 4-bit or 8-bit or 16-bit or 32-bit registers.

All data entering a microprocessor go into a register and all the data leaving it depart from a register. In between entering and leaving, the data are processed in other parts of the microprocessor.

The Spectrum microcomputer uses the Z80 microprocessor while the BBC microcomputer uses the 6502. Both of them have 8-bit registers. We will look at each microcomputer and microprocessor in turn.

☐ Machine Code and the Spectrum's Z80 Microprocessor

The Z80 microprocessor has a lot of registers. Those used most frequently are known as the A, B, C, D, E, F, H and L registers, as in Fig. 13.1. Each of them is an 8-bit register. Chief among them is the **A register**. It is also called the **accumulator**. Many instructions in the instruction

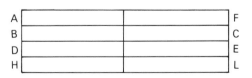

Fig. 13.1   The registers in a Z80 microprocessor

set refer to the accumulator. The result of carrying out many of the instructions is put in the A register. For example, if the microprocessor adds two 8-bit numbers, the answer is put in the accumulator.

The B, C, D, E, H and L registers are **secondary registers**. They can work individually as 8-bit registers. If necessary, they can pair up, B and C, D and E, H and L, to form 16-bit registers. The secondary registers have been designed to be better at some jobs than others. For example, the B and C registers are good at counting, the H and L registers are good at pointing to memory locations. A programmer needs to remember this.

The **F register** is the **flags register**. Two of its eight bits are not used. Each of the remaining six bits signals a different message to other parts of the microprocessor, just as a flag flying at half-mast signals a message to people. For example, one bit is the **zero flag**. It is used when the microprocessor is counting down. The bit goes to logic 1 when the count has reached zero. This tells the microprocessor to stop counting and get on with the next job.

□ **Giving Instructions to the Spectrum's Z80 Microprocessor**

A very simple task for the microprocessor is to make it add one and one and display the answer on the 8-bit indicator.

The instructions for this task have to tell the microprocessor exactly what to do. What the instructions will say is:

'Load 1 into your accumulator. Load 1 into your B register. Now add the numbers in your A and B registers. Finally, output the answer (which will be in the accumulator) to the Interpack output port.'

These instructions are stored in the RAM as a series of binary numbers. Fortunately, we can key in the numbers in hex! The instruction numbers are given in the microprocessor's handbook.

The hex code for 'Load the accumulator with a number' is 3E. This is entered on the keyboard. It is followed by the hex value of the number, 01 in this case. Thus, the complete keyboard entry for

'Load the accumulator with 1'
is
3E 01

The hex code for 'Load the B register with a number' is 06. This is entered on the keyboard and followed by the hex number, 01 again. So, the complete keyboard entry for

'Load the B register with 1'
is
06 01

The complete keyboard entry for

'Add the A and B registers'
is
80

The hex code for 'Output the number in the accumulator' is D3. This is entered on the keyboard and is followed by the address of the Interpack output port, 5FH (95 in decimal). The complete keyboard entry for

'Output number in accumulator to Interpack output port'
is
D3 5F

Four points should be noted:

1 the accumulator must be one of the two registers used;

2 when the instructions are obeyed, the microprocessor puts the answer, 02H, in the accumulator;

3 the accumulator still contains the answer after it has told the output port what it is;

4 the original number in the B register is unchanged.

□ Memory Location Addresses in the Spectrum

The programmer has to tell the microprocessor the address of the RAM memory locations in which it is to store the instructions as they are keyed in. Usually, it is enough to give the address of the location where the first instruction is to be stored. The microprocessor carries on from there by itself.

Activity 13 gives some machine code programs for the Spectrum. The first machine code instruction in each program is stored in the RAM location with the address EA60H (60 000 in decimal).

□ Tabulate Programs

Machine code programs must be set out in tabular form. Table 13.1 shows how the program for adding two numbers is tabulated.

Memory location	Memory contents	Mnemonic	Comment
EA60	3E 01	LDA, 01	Load accumulator with 01H.
EA62	06 01	LDB, 01	Load B register with 01H.
EA64	80	ADD A,B	Add the A and B registers.
EA65	D3 5F	OUT(5F), A	Output number in accumulator to Interpack output port, address 5F.

Table 13.1   Program for adding two numbers (Spectrum/Z80)

The **memory location column** gives the address in the RAM where each instruction is stored.

The **memory contents column** gives the hexadecimal value of the binary number stored in a memory location. Each location can hold an 8-bit binary number, a byte.

The first instruction, 'Load the accumulator with 01' needs two locations, EA60H and EA61H. This is because the full instruction is two bytes long, i.e. 3E and 01. Some instructions are one byte long, others are three bytes long. It is customary to put the full instruction on one line of a table and quote only the first of the memory locations it occupies.

The **mnemonic column** gives a shorthand version of each instruction. The mnemonics have an exact form which is set out in the microprocessor's handbook. When programming in assembly language, mnemonics are entered on the keyboard.

The **comment column** is most important. It is for the programmer's own summary of what each instruction or section of the program is meant to do. Whatever programming language is in use, comments are essential. Without them, the program will not mean anything to other people. Worse still, after a few days it will not mean anything to you, the programmer!

□   **Entering Machine Code into the Spectrum**

One way of getting a machine code program into the Spectrum is with the help of a BASIC program. This program is called a **machine code loader**, as in Program 13.1 overleaf. The machine code program is included in the BASIC program as DATA at line 2010. When the BASIC program is RUN, it loads the machine code into the chosen memory locations. Once this is done, the BASIC program hands over to the machine code program (line 80) and that program is executed.

The last entry, 'C9', in line 2010 of Program 13.1, is an additional item and is very important. It is the code for the 'Return' (RET) instruction. It makes the machine code program hand back to BASIC once its job is done.

In some assignments in Activity 13 we shall want the machine code program to execute only once. In these cases, the computer gives a STOP report (line 100 of Program 13.1) just after the machine code has handed back to BASIC.

In other assignments, the machine code programs are endless loops, for example, the 8-bit binary count program. In these cases, line 100 of Program 13.1 is altered to make the BASIC hand straight back to the machine code for another run through that program. The necessary details are given in the assignments.

You should SAVE Program 13.1 on tape, microdrive cartridge or floppy disc. You should also SAVE each Activity program once you have keyed in its line 2010 DATA.

```
  10 CLEAR 59999
  20 RESTORE 2010
  30 LET address = 60000
  40 CLS: PRINT "LOADING MACHINE CODE PROGRAM": PRINT
  50 GO TO 1800
  60 GO SUB 200
  80 RANDOMIZE USR 60000
 100 STOP
 200 PRINT "MACHINE CODE PROGRAM WILL RUN"
 210 PRINT "IN 1 SECOND FROM NOW.": PRINT
 220 PAUSE 50
 230 PRINT "MACHINE CODE PROGRAM RUNNING."
 240 RETURN
1800 LET data = 0
1810 READ h$
1820 IF h$ = "end of code." THEN GO TO 60
1830 LET n = LEN h$
1840 IF n < > 2*INT (n/2) THEN CLS: PRINT "odd number of hex.
     digits in :";h$: PRINT"type LIST 2010": STOP
1850 LET p = 1
1860 LET m = 1
1870 LET a$ = h$(p)
1880 IF NOT ((a$ > = "0" AND a$ < = "9") OR (a$ > = "A" AND a$ < = "F"))
     THEN CLS: PRINT "non hex. digit: ";a$;" in ";h$: PRINT'
     "type LIST 2010": STOP
1890 LET b = CODE a$
1900 IF b < = 57 THEN LET c = b − 48: GO TO 1920
1910 IF b < = 70 THEN LET c = b − 55
1920 LET data = data + c*16 ∧ m
1930 LET p = p + 1
1940 IF m = 0 THEN POKE address,data: LET address = address + 1: LET
     data = 0: LET m = 1: GO TO 1960
1950 LET m = 0
1960 IF p > n THEN GO TO 2000
1970 GO TO 1870
2000 GO TO 1800
2010 DATA "3E01","0601","80","D35F","C9"
2020 DATA "end of code."
```

Program 13.1   Machine code loader (Spectrum). Note: includes specimen DATA at line 2010

☐ Machine Code and the BBC's 6502 Microprocessor

The 6502 microprocessor has fewer registers than the Z80 microprocessor.

Those most frequently used are the A, X and Y registers, as in Fig. 13.2. Each of them is an 8-bit register. The **A register** is called the **accumulator**. Many instructions in the instruction set refer to the accumulator.

Fig. 13.2   The registers in a 6502 microprocessor

The BBC computer is designed so that some of the locations in its random access memory, RAM, work specially closely with the microprocessor. For example, memory location &FE6F is used as a **flags register**. One of its eight bits is not used. The seven remaining bits are used to signal different messages to the microprocessor, just as a flag flying at half-mast signals a message to people. For example, one bit is the **zero flag**. If the answer to something the microprocessor has just worked out is zero, this bit is set to logic 1. This can tell the microprocessor that it should now get on with the next job. Another bit is the **carry flag**. It is set to logic 1 if the answer to, say, a calculation is greater than 255 (decimal).

☐ Giving Instructions to the BBC's 6502 Microprocessor

A very simple task for the microprocessor is to make it add one and one and display the answer on the 8-bit indicator.

The instructions for this task have to tell the microprocessor exactly what to do. What the instructions will say is:

'Load 1 into your accumulator. Make sure the carry flag is reset to logic 0 (if it is set to logic 1 the answer to the calculation will be one greater than the correct answer). Now add 1 to the accumulator. Finally, output the answer (which will be in the accumulator) to the Interpack output port.'

These instructions are stored in the RAM as a series of binary numbers. Fortunately, we can key in the numbers in hex! The instruction numbers are given in the microprocessor's handbook.

The hex code for 'Load the accumulator with a number' is A9. This is entered on the keyboard. It is then followed by the hex value of the number, 01 in this case. Thus, the complete keyboard entry for

'Load the accumulator with 1'

is

A9 01

The hex code for 'Clear the carry flag, i.e. reset it to logic 0' is 18. So, the complete keyboard entry for

'Clear the carry flag'
is
18

The hex code for 'Add a number to the number already in the accumulator' is 69. This is entered on the keyboard. It is followed by the hex value of the number, 01 in this case. Thus, the complete keyboard entry for

'Add 1 to the accumulator'
is
69 01

The hex code for 'Output (or 'Store') the number in the accumulator' is 8D. This is entered on the keyboard and is followed by the address of the Interpack output port, FCC2. So, the complete keyboard entry for

'Output number in accumulator to Interpack output port'
is
8D C2FC

Four points should be noted:

1   notice how the Interpack output port address must be entered. The two least significant digits (the **low-order byte**), C2, must be entered first and then the two most significant digits (the **high-order byte**), FC. This is called **reverse byte order** and must be used whenever an address is part of an instruction to a 6502 microprocessor.

2   all arithmetic involves the accumulator.

3   when the instructions are obeyed, the microprocessor puts the answer, 02, in the accumulator.

4   the accumulator still contains the answer after it has told the output port what it is.

☐   **Memory Location Addresses in the BBC**

The programmer has to tell the microprocessor the address of the RAM memory locations in which it is to store the instructions as they are keyed in. Usually, it is enough to give the address of the location where the first instruction is to be stored. The microprocessor carries on from there by itself.

Activity 13 gives some machine code programs for the BBC computer. The first machine code instruction in each program is stored in the RAM location

168

with the hex address &5000. (Note: the BBC computer convention is to identify hexadecimal numbers with an ampersand sign, &; for example, &5000.)

☐ Tabulate Programs

Machine code programs must be set out in tabular form. Table 13.2 shows how the program for adding two numbers is tabulated.

Memory location	Memory contents	Mnemonic	Comment
5000	A9 01	LDA#01	Load accumulator with &01.
5002	18	CLC	Clear carry flag to zero.
5003	69 01	ADC#01	Add &01 to accumulator.
5005	8D C2FC	STA FCC2	Store number in accumulator at address FCC2, Interpack output port.

Table 13.2   Program for adding two numbers (BBC/6502)

The **memory location column** gives the address in the RAM where each instruction is stored.

The **memory contents column** gives the hexadecimal value of the binary number stored in a memory location. Each location can hold an 8-bit binary number, a byte.

The first instruction, 'Load the accumulator with 1' needs two locations, &5000 and &5001. This is because the full instruction is two bytes long, i.e. A9 and 01. Some instructions are one byte long, others are three bytes long. It is customary to put the full instruction on one line of the table and quote only the first of the memory locations it occupies.

The **mnemonic column** gives a shorthand version of each instruction. The mnemonics have an exact form which is set out in the microprocessor's handbook. When programming in assembly language, mnemonics are entered on the keyboard.

The **comment column** is most important. It is for the programmer's own summary of what each instruction or section of the program is meant to do. Whatever programming language is in use, comments are essential. Without them, the program will not mean anything to other people. Worse still, after a few days it will not mean anything to you, the programmer!

☐ Entering Machine Code into the BBC

One way of getting a machine code program into the BBC computer is with the help of a BASIC program. This program is called a **machine code loader**, as in Program 13.2. The machine code program is included in the BASIC program as DATA at line 2010. When the BASIC program is RUN, it loads

```
  10 HIMEM = &4FFF
  20 RESTORE 2010
  30 LET address = &5000
  40 CLS: PRINT "LOADING MACHINE CODE PROGRAM": PRINT
  50 GOTO 1800
  60 GOSUB 200
  80 CALL &5000
 100 STOP
 200 PRINT "MACHINE CODE PROGRAM WILL RUN"
 210 PRINT "IN 1 SECOND FROM NOW.": PRINT
 220 TIME = 0: REPEAT UNTIL TIME = 100
 230 PRINT "MACHINE CODE PROGRAM RUNNING."
 240 RETURN
1800 LET data = 0
1810 READ h$
1820 IF h$ = "end of code." THEN GOTO 60
1830 LET n = LEN (h$)
1840 IF n < > 2*INT (n/2) THEN CLS: PRINT "odd number of hex.
digits in :";h$: PRINT"type LIST 2010": STOP
1850 LET p = 1
1860 LET m = 1
1870 LET a$ = MID$(h$,p,1)
1880 IF NOT ((a$ > = "0" AND a$ < = "9") OR (a$ > = "A" AND a$ < = "F"))
     THEN CLS: PRINT "non hex. digit: ";a$;" in ";h$:
     PRINT"type LIST 2010": STOP
1890 LET b = ASC a$
1900 IF b < = 57 THEN LET c = b - 48: GOTO 1920
1910 IF b < = 70 THEN LET c = b - 55
1920 LET data = data + c*16 ∧
1930 LET p = p + 1
1940 IF m = 0 THEN ?address = data: LET address = address + 1: LET data = 0: LET
     m = 1: GOTO 1960
1950 LET m = 0
1960 IF p > n THEN GOTO 2000
1970 GOTO 1870
2000 GOTO 1800
2010 DATA "A901","18","6901","8DC2FC","60"
2020 DATA "end of code."
```

Program 13.2   Machine code loader (BBC). Note: includes specimen DATA at line
                2010

the machine code into the chosen memory locations. Once this is done, the BASIC program hands over to the machine code program (line 80) and that program is executed.

The last entry, '60', in line 2010 of Program 13.2, is an additional item and is very important. It is the code for the 'Return from subroutine' (RTS) instruction. It makes the machine code program hand back to BASIC once its job is done.

In some assignments in Activity 13 we shall want the machine code program to execute only once. In these cases, the computer gives a STOP report (line 100 of Program 13.2) just after the machine code has handed back to BASIC.

In other assignments, the machine code programs are endless loops, for example, the 8-bit binary count program. In these cases, line 100 of Program 13.2 is altered to make the BASIC hand straight back to the machine code for another run through that program. The necessary details are given in the assignments.

You should SAVE Program 13.2 on tape or disc. You should also SAVE each Activity program once you have keyed in its line 2010 DATA.

14 Circuit Design, Construction and Testing

Electronic circuits which do not work can be the cause of a lot of frustration and heartache. The first line of defence is to avoid problems through sound knowledge of digital microelectronic devices, careful design and development work, first class craftsmanship and attention to detail. The second line of defence is an ability to test a circuit methodically.

☐ Design

Every complex system is nothing more than a number of simple systems strung together. For example, Fig. 14.1 shows the essential parts of an electronic stopwatch. Each part can be analysed further. For example, Fig. 14.2 shows an analysis of the accurate low frequency clock. Fig. 14.3 shows an analysis of the count and display system.

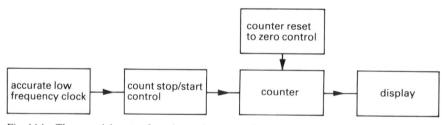

Fig. 14.1   The essential parts of an electronic stopwatch

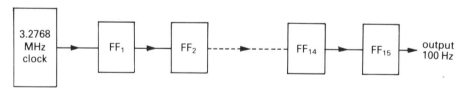

Fig. 14.2   Analysis of an accurate low frequency clock

When a system has been fully analysed, **circuit diagrams** can produced for each part. As the diagrams are drawn, check the **operating requirements** of each integrated circuit. For example, which pins are the power supply pins; are there inputs which must be pulled up to logic 1 or pulled down to logic 0; what must be done with the unused inputs of logic gates; are clock inputs active high or active low; which edge of a pulse is the active edge?

172

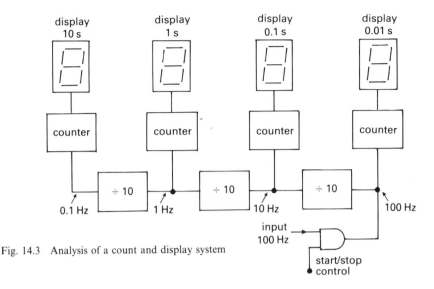

Fig. 14.3   Analysis of a count and display system

As each circuit is designed, it should be built on the logic board or on some other **bread boarding system** and tested to prove that it is correct. Only then should one part of the system be connected to the next part. This assembly should be proved before a third part is connected and tested, and so on.

☐   Circuit Diagrams

A large, clear circuit diagram of the tested system is essential. The circuit diagram must be accurate and up to date. The testing and development of a circuit always results in **modifications**. They must be put on the diagram immediately. It will never be done if you leave it till later. This will cause untold frustration and confusion as your hardware and your drawing will not agree. You will not be able to remember what you did or why you did it.

Always **photocopy** a master circuit diagram before updating it. You may need to retrace your steps. Label the copy of the original master circuit diagram 'Issue 1'. Label the modified master circuit diagram 'Issue 2' and note the date of the modification too.

☐   Planning Construction

There are several **circuit construction techniques**. All involve mounting and interconnecting components. It is not easy to mount components so that one does not run out of space or produce a tangle of wires. These problems may be avoided if a layout is sketched on paper. Start from the diagram which defined the essential parts of the system, e.g. Fig. 14.1. Allow space for each part in proportion to the number and size of the components in it. Place the parts so that they relate naturally to each other. But, take account of the actual position of the inputs and outputs of integrated circuits.

To reduce the chance of incorrect connections being made, place the integrated circuits the same way round, for example, every pin 1 in the top, left-hand position. The direction chosen will be the one which gives the most convenient flow of connections from one part of the system to another.

☐ Solderless Breadboards

Always prove a circuit design by assembling and testing it on a **prototyping system**, e.g. the logic board or a solderless breadboard (Fig. 14.4).

On a solderless breadboard, components and interconnecting wires push into contact strips below the surface of the board. Each strip has a number of contacts, often five. This allows several components to be connected together.

There is a long strip of contacts down each edge of the breadboards. They are used as the 0 V and positive supply rails. Label the rails so that connection errors are avoided. Which strip is used for which rail depends on which way round the integrated circuits are placed. Designate the rails to give the easiest 0 V and positive connections to the chips.

Insert the integrated circuits and any discrete components in accordance with the planning sketch. Use a photocopy of the master circuit diagram as a guide when interconnecting the components. As each component is installed and as each connection is made, tick it off on the photocopy.

Begin by making all of the 0 V and positive rail connections. Use insulated wire with a single solid conductor. Only use multistranded wire for connections which go off a circuit board. Use wires with different coloured

Fig. 14.4   Circuit on solderless breadboard

insulation for specific tasks: for example, red for all positive rail connections, black for all 0 V connections. Make wires run down the board or across it. Do not let them run diagonally. Take care to make each wire the right length for its job. Make sure that the insulation goes right up to the edge of the hole through which the bare end passes to the contacts beneath.

Double check every connection. When you think you have finished, carefully check the circuit diagram to make sure no connection has been omitted. Check everything before powering the system.

Full instructions for its use are supplied with a solderless breadboard. There will be a maximum diameter of wire or component lead which a contact can accept. It is essential that this measurement is not exceeded because the contact will be strained. It will fail to make a good connection when used later with a wire of smaller diameter. This will certainly cause much frustration and waste of time.

☐ Permanent Circuits — Veroboard

When a circuit has been drawn and proved, a permanent version with soldered connections can be built. Much of the layout method used on solderless breadboards should be observed when making a **permanent circuit**. Components can be mounted on various types of circuit board.

Fig. 14.5   The underside of various circuit boards

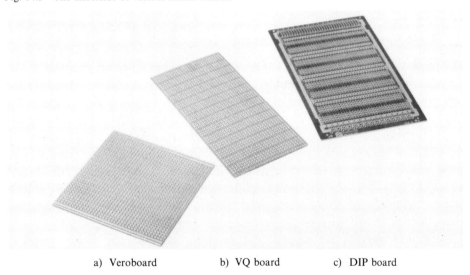

a) Veroboard   b) VQ board   c) DIP board

Veroboard is a board of resin bonded paper with a matrix of holes at 0.1″ pitch. One side of the board is plain. The other side has copper strips running its length linking rows of holes, as in Fig. 14.5a. Components are mounted on the plain side of the board. Their leads pass through holes to the copper strips to which they are soldered.

Veroboard is supplied with a circuit connection planning sheet. The planning, building and testing of anything other than the simplest of circuits is difficult. Connection involves not only the making of soldered joints but also the breaking of copper tracks. This doubles the chance of an error. A broken copper strip can have near-invisible whiskers at its ends. These can touch an adjacent strip causing a short circuit. It is all too easy to bridge adjacent tracks when soldering. A non-functioning circuit is difficult to check and rectify because the connections are on both sides of the board. Their routes may be difficult to follow.

☐   Permanent Circuits — VQ Board

VQ board is similar to Veroboard but its copper strips do not run the full length of the board. They are in short sections so that each strip links four holes, as in Fig. 14.5b. A successful circuit can be transferred directly from a solderless breadboard, as in Fig. 14.4, to VQ board. All connections are on the component side of the board. It is not necessary to make additional breaks in copper strips.

A disadvantage of VQ board is that it does not have continuous copper strips down each edge to serve as power supply rails. This can be overcome by 'daisy-chaining' strips with short pieces of wire soldered in place or by making solder bridges. In view of the small amount of copper around a hole in a strip, it is recommended that two rows of strips on each edge of the board are joined in parallel to make substantial power rails.

☐   Permanent Circuits — DIP Board

DIP (dual-in-line pin) board, as in Fig. 14.5c, is used extensively in industry for permanent connection of 'one-off' systems. It is made from resin bonded paper or from glass reinforced plastic (GRP) sheet. The board has a matrix of holes on a 0.1″ pitch. A copper strip runs down each edge. At regular intervals, branches from each strip cross the board side by side for almost its full width. These parallel strips are the 0 V and positive power supply rails. They run parallel to the integrated circuits on the board. This makes connection of chips to the power rails straightforward. The power supply strips are duplicated on the component side of the board. They may be linked with short pieces of wire to make more substantial conductors.

Integrated circuits are placed in rows between the cross-board pairs of power supply strips. They are soldered to short copper strips, as in Fig. 14.6. Connections between components are made by linking the appropriate short copper strips with single solid conductor insulated wire. The wire is on the component side of the board. Its stripped ends are passed through holes in the board and soldered.

Size for size, DIP board costs more than Veroboard or VQ board but the extra cost is more than justified by the ease of assembly, checking and alteration it affords.

Fig. 14.6 Components on DIP board

□ Permanent Circuits — Printed Circuit Boards

A **printed circuit board (PCB)** is the best means of permanently connecting a system. The board is made from resin bonded paper or glass reinforced plastic. It has **copper foil** glued to one or both sides. The copper foil can be selectively **etched** away with **ferric chloride solution** to leave a pattern of **copper tracks**, as in Fig. 14.7a. These, rather than wires, connect the components in the required manner, as in Fig. 14.7b.

Copper foil which is not to be etched away is protected with a **resist**. This may be cellulose paint applied by hand with a fine brush or with a special felt-tip pen. Alternatively, the resist can be special rub-down transfers applied to the copper foil in the required track pattern. Track patterns for a complex system are transferred to the copper by a method similar to that used to produce a photographic print.

Fig. 14.7 A printed circuit board

a) Track side

b) Component side

The design of a PCB track layout involves a great deal of work. Often professional draughtsmen do not get it right first time. Sometimes a PCB with an error can be 'fiddled' into usefulness but, all too often, the work must be done again.

Computer-aided Design (CAD) systems are being used more and more by industry to help draughtsmen produce PCB layouts quickly and easily. Good PCB design programs are now available for computers found in schools. A school could use such a program to build up a library of useful sub-circuits, e.g., a 7-segment display circuit, a counter circuit, an R-S flip-flop circuit. It would then be a simple matter for you to take from the library the sub-circuits you need for a project, position and link them on the VDU screen and then get a print-out which could be used to make your own PCB.

PCBs are ideal when many identical circuits are required. They save time and make it possible for unskilled people or machines to assemble circuits correctly. When only one circuit is required, design of a complex PCB layout without a CAD system to help you is not worth the time and effort. If it is attempted, it is for the sake of the neat, professional appearance of the finished product.

☐ **Ferric Chloride**

Be sure to use only ferric chloride hexahydrate as some forms of ferric chloride can be dangerous when mixed with water.

Ferric chloride must be handled with care. Apart from its ability to stain, it is **corrosive** and should not be allowed to touch the skin. You should *wear rubber gloves, laboratory goggles and an overall* when working with it.

Ferric chloride can be bought as a ready-to-use solution or as solid lumps. The solid material must be stored in a leak-proof sealed plastic container to prevent it from absorbing atmospheric moisture and producing droplets of solution. A satisfactory etchant solution can be made from 500 grams of ferric chloride in 1 litre of water (ten ounces in one pint). Place the solid ferric chloride in a plastic bucket and dissolve it in the appropriate quantity of warm water. Store the solution in a sealed and labelled chemical bottle.

When required for use, the etchant should be poured into a shallow plastic dish which is itself sitting in a dish of hot water. The PCB to be etched should have smooth edges with no burrs. It is slid sideways, copper side down, on to the surface of the etchant so that it floats. This is to allow iron, precipitated during the etching process, to fall to the bottom of the dish. Provided the PCB has smooth edges and is not put straight down on to the solution, air bubbles will not be trapped under it. With fresh, warm solution, a PCB can be etched in about 15 minutes. As the solution becomes exhausted, the etching time increases and the solution changes colour from dark brown to dark green. Ask your chemistry teacher about how you should dispose of exhausted solution safely.

When etching is complete, wash the PCB in cold running water.

☐ Cleaning a Circuit Board

The greatest cause of circuit malfunction is poor quality soldered joints. These are the result of dirt on one or more of the surfaces to be soldered. Before soldering commences, the copper tracks on any type of circuit board must be polished with a **track cleaning block** until they are bright. An alternative to a track cleaning block is an ink or a typist's eraser. Do not use emery cloth or glass paper. Do not touch the polished tracks with the fingers. Dust the tracks and then spray them with a **PCB track lacquer**. This protects the copper and maintains optimum solderability for a long period of time.

☐ Tools

Circuit construction does not require many tools: small snipe nose pliers with smooth jaws, small wire cutters (top or side cutting), an adjustable wire stripper, a small screwdriver, a soldering iron and a desoldering pump.

A 17 watt **soldering iron** with a fine bit is ideal for most work. The bit of the iron must be kept clean. Wipe the bit frequently on a damp sponge. A sponge is usually supplied with a **soldering iron stand**. The end of the bit should always be wet and bright with a thin film of fresh solder.

A **desoldering pump** is used to suck molten solder away from a joint when a component has to be removed from a circuit board. Without a desoldering pump, it is difficult to remove an integrated circuit from a circuit board.

☐ Soldering

Resin cored solder for electronic work is available in various grades and diameters. The lower melting point 60/40 tin/lead solder is suitable for most purposes. The smaller diameter 22 gauge solder is most convenient for integrated circuit work.

When soldering, hold the iron like a pen and not like a poker. Put the bit on the circuit board track and slide it up to the wire or pin to be soldered. The track and the pin must be heated equally. The flat of the bit should be in contact with the pin. Feed solder into the corner made by the track and the pin so that first the flux in the solder and then the solder itself flow over both parts. Add enough solder to completely surround the pin. Then, remove the solder supply from the joint and, half a second later, when the molten solder has settled, remove the soldering iron bit. Do not move the soldered parts while the solder is freezing. Let the solder freeze naturally: do not blow on it. A good soldered joint should be smooth, bright and the shape of a cone with slightly concave sides. Always inspect each joint as it is made.

☐ Integrated Circuit Sockets

The cheapest **sockets** cost nearly as much as the cheapest digital integrated circuits. But it is worth using them rather than soldering the chips in place.

The chips are kept safe until they are really needed while fault-finding and correction is much easier.

Sockets must be soldered on to a circuit board the same way round as the integrated circuits. They always have a notch or a chamfered corner or a moulding mark which identifies the end of the socket which accepts pin 1 of the chip.

The pins of chips may need to be bent inwards a little before they can be inserted in a socket. Hold the pins on one side of a chip against a flat surface. Gently press down and twist the chip package so that all of the pins bend together. Repeat the process on the other row of pins.

Ease the chip into its socket only when the power supply is off. Make sure pin 1 is in the right place. Check that all pins have entered the socket. An odd one may curl round under the chip.

Remove a chip from a socket only when the power supply is off. Gently ease it up, a little at a time at either end, with a small screwdriver. Better still, use a chip removal tool. Above all, don't pull it straight out with your fingers. You will stab yourself with the pins and bend them too!

☐ Checks

If a circuit does not function, always suspect your work first. Blame the electronic components as the very last resort! Many problems may be avoided if the following checks are made as a circuit is constructed:

1 is the soldering first class with no dry joints or solder splashes or solder runs?
2 are the right components in the right place and the right way round?
3 has a pin of an integrated circuit curled round underneath the chip instead of entering the socket?
4 do all the interconnections really agree with the circuit diagram?
5 is there a hair-line break in a copper track?
6 has the lead of a resistor been bent so close to the body that it is partially detached?
7 is a stray strand of multistranded wire causing a short circuit?

These checks should be repeated if a circuit fails to work. In addition, check that the power supply is working. Is it connected to the circuit? Is its polarity correct? Is it set to the right voltage? Can it supply enough current?

Do not make assumptions. Check every connection, especially 'the obvious ones'!

☐ Testing with a Multimeter

A powered, but non-functioning, circuit may be tested with a **multimeter**, as in Fig. 14.8. Many people find the quicker response of an **analogue meter**, as in Fig. 14.8a, makes it more convenient than a **digital meter**, as in Fig. 14.8b,

Fig. 14.8   Multimeters

a) An
   analogue
   multimeter

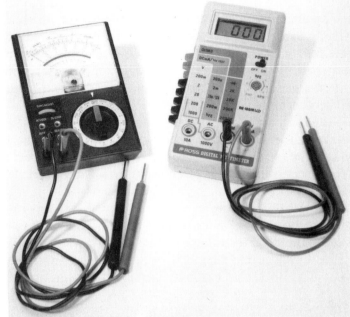

b) A digital
   multimeter

for testing a circuit. The multimeter is set to a voltage range which just covers the supply voltage for the integrated circuits being used.

A first test is to check that all integrated circuit sockets are connected to the power supply. With the power supply turned off, remove all of the integrated circuits from their sockets. With the system powered, the black probe of the meter is connected to the 0 V position on a socket. The red probe is connected to the V_{cc} supply position on the socket. The meter should indicate the voltage of the power supply, 5 V for TTL chips. All of the sockets are tested in this manner.

A second test is to see that positions on each socket which should be pulled up to the supply voltage or tied down to 0 V are at the right logic level. With the red probe connected to the V_{cc} position, use the black probe to test each position which should be at 0 V. The meter should give supply voltage readings. Then, with the black probe connected to the 0 V position, use the red probe to test each position which should be pulled up to logic 1. The meter should give supply voltage readings or slightly less. The exact value depends on whether the pull-up is achieved by direct connection to the supply or whether a pull-up resistor has been used.

It is wise to make these first two tests part of a routine inspection procedure for all newly completed circuit boards. Because some integrated circuits can be destroyed if operated while not properly connected to the power supply, the tests should be conducted before the chips are installed and powered for the first time.

With the integrated circuits in place and the system powered, a multimeter can be used to check that the outputs of logic gates change logic level as expected. Connect the black probe of the multimeter to the 0 V line of the system. Check the output of each gate by holding the red probe on the appropriate pin and reading the meter. The meter will read 0 V when the output is at logic 0 and about 3.3 V or the supply voltage (depending on whether the chips are TTL or CMOS) if the output is at logic 1. Input logic levels are checked in the same way.

It is important to be systemmatic and methodical when making these logic level tests. With the help of the circuit diagram, start at the point where signals go into the system. Work through the system to where it produces its output. At every position tested, you must know what the logic level ought to be. Repeat the process for all possible combinations of input logic level. When you get a meter reading different from what was expected, you have found the fault. Its cause is another matter!

Start to trace the cause by testing the chip which shows the fault. Remove it from the circuit (power off first!), insert it in a socket on the logic board and test it thoroughly. If the chip is sound, test all other chips directly connected to it.

Persevere. Trouble-shooting can take a long time. Often it is a case of the simpler the fault, the longer the time!

☐ Testing with a Logic Probe

All of the multimeter tests may be made more quickly and easily with a **logic probe**, as in Fig. 14.9a.

Fig. 14.9   A logic probe

a) A three-LED and a
   multi-LED logic probe

b) A logic probe in use

The leads from the top of the probe are connected to the power supply of the circuit under test. In the body of a simple logic probe are a red and a green light-emitting diode. Normally, neither LED is on. However, if the needle point of the probe is touched on a part of a circuit, as in Fig. 14.9b, which is at logic 1 or the positive supply voltage, the red LED turns on. If the needle is touched on a part of the circuit which is at logic 0 or 0 V, the green LED turns on. It is important that a logic probe is suitable for the type of integrated circuit (TTL or CMOS) used in the system being tested.

Some logic probes have a very useful third, amber, LED which is on only if the needle is not touching anything or is touching a disconnected part of a circuit. Other logic probes may have a display with a large number of LEDs which gives a moderately skilled user much useful information.

☐ **Testing Clocks**

An analogue multimeter, as in Fig. 14.8a, or a logic probe, as in Fig. 14.9, can be used to test for the presence of a stream of clock pulses. A digital meter, as in Fig. 14.8b, is not suitable: it cannot respond quickly enough.

If the red probe of a multimeter is connected to the output of a low frequency clock circuit, say 2 Hz, the needle of the meter will move backwards and forwards from 0 V to the logic 1 voltage. If a logic probe is used instead of a meter, its green and red LEDs will turn on and off alternately.

If the clock is running at a slightly higher frequency, say 50 Hz, the needle of the meter will quiver around a voltage reading about half way between 0 V and the logic 1 voltage. The higher the clock frequency, the less the needle will quiver. The precise value of the reading depends on the mark-space ratio of the clock pulses. If the mark is longer than the space, the meter reading will be above the half-way value. If the mark is shorter than the space, the meter reading will be below the half-way value.

If a logic probe is connected to the output of a clock running at, say, 50 Hz, both the green and red LEDs will appear to be illuminated simultaneously but not at full brightness. If the mark is longer than the space, the red LED will be slightly brighter than the green LED. If the mark is shorter than the space, the red LED will be slightly dimmer than the green LED.

☐ **Testing with an Oscilloscope**

All of the multimeter and logic probe tests may be made with an **oscilloscope**, as in Fig. 14.10. An oscilloscope is more versatile than the other two test instruments and it can give more information about a circuit's performance. At first sight, an oscilloscope looks very complicated because it has so many controls. However, only two of the controls are essential. The other controls provide useful refinements.

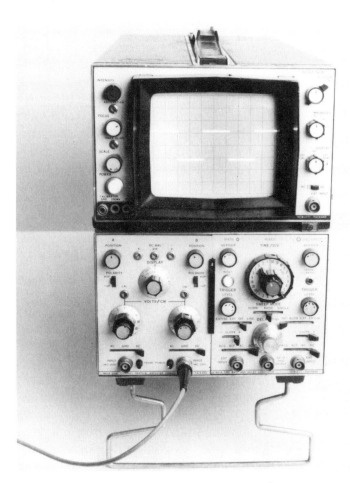

Fig. 14.10
An oscilloscope

An oscilloscope belongs to the same family as a television set or a visual display unit (VDU) for a computer. In a television set, an electron beam strikes the phosphor coating on the back of the glass screen. As a result, a small, bright spot appears on the screen. The spot moves across the screen in response to signals from the broadcasting station and creates the pictures which we watch. Sometimes the bright spot can be seen in the middle of the screen for a few seconds just after the television set has been switched off. With a VDU, the bright spot moves across the back of the screen in response to a signal from a computer and creates writing or graphics displays. With an oscilloscope, the bright spot can move across the back of the screen in response to any signal we supply to the instrument.

Imagine that the oscilloscope is switched on and the bright spot is in the centre of the screen. If the **vertical position control** or **Y control**, as in Fig. 14.11c, is rotated backwards and forwards, the spot moves up and down the screen. Imagine that the vertical position control has moved the spot to position A, as in Fig. 14.11a. This position, or any other vertical position we choose, can be a **zero position**. From the chosen zero position, vertical movements of the spot up or down the screen may be **measured**.

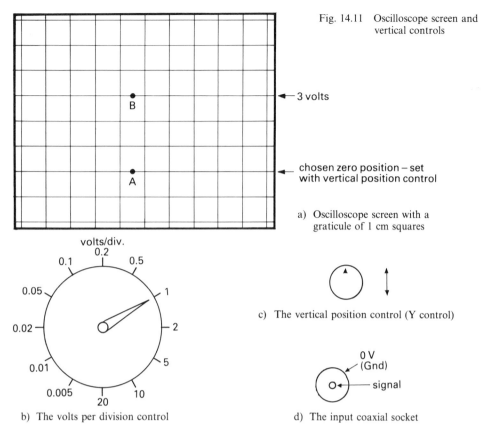

Fig. 14.11 Oscilloscope screen and vertical controls

- 3 volts

- chosen zero position – set with vertical position control

a) Oscilloscope screen with a graticule of 1 cm squares

c) The vertical position control (Y control)

volts/div.

b) The volts per division control

0 V (Gnd)

signal

d) The input coaxial socket

The spot is made to move vertically away from the selected zero position by a signal fed into the oscilloscope at its input socket. This is a coaxial socket, as in Fig. 14.11d, and is usually of the **BNC** type. If the inner signal socket is made more positive than the outer 0 V or ground (Gnd) socket, the spot moves up the screen. If the inner signal socket is made more negative than the outer 0 V socket, the spot moves down the screen. This may be demonstrated by connecting the terminals of a battery to the input socket. Start with the positive pole of the battery connected to the signal socket and the 0 V or negative pole of the battery connected to the 0 V socket. The spot moves up the screen. Reverse the battery connections and the spot moves down the screen.

The extent to which the spot moves away from the zero position in response to an input voltage is governed by the **volts per division control**, as in Fig. 14.11b. If this control is set to 1 volt per division and the input is made 3 V more positive than the 0 V input, the spot will move from position A to position B, as in Fig. 14.11a. If the signal is removed, the spot returns to position A. If the volts per division control is reset to 0.5 volts/div and the 3 V signal reapplied, the spot will move up six divisions from position A. If the volts per division control is reset to 2 volts/div the spot will move up 1.5 divisions from position A. When used in this manner, the oscilloscope is being treated as an analogue voltmeter and the volts per division control is its range selection switch.

Imagine that the oscilloscope is switched on, the **time-base control**, as in Fig. 14.12b, is off and the bright spot is in the centre of the screen. If the **horizontal position control** or **X control**, as in Fig. 14.12c, is rotated backwards and forwards, the spot moves from left to right to left across the screen.

Fig. 14.12   Oscilloscope screen and horizontal controls

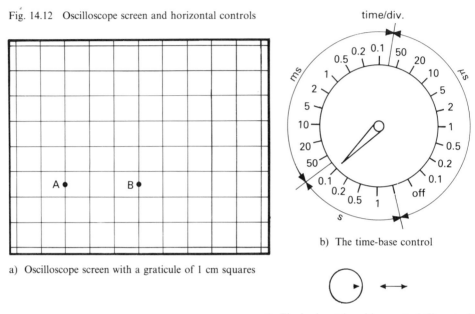

a) Oscilloscope screen with a graticule of 1 cm squares

b) The time-base control

c) The horizontal position control (X control)

The spot can be made to move automatically across the screen from far left to far right by a signal which is generated by the oscilloscope itself. The time-base control, as in Fig. 14.12b, sets the time taken by the spot to traverse one division of the screen graticule, as in Fig. 14.12a, from left to right. If the time-base control is set to 0.1 s/div, it takes the spot 0.3 of a second to move the three divisions from position A to position B. Once the spot has reached the right-hand side of the screen, it almost instantly begins the next traverse from left to right. The return of the spot to the left is not visible on the screen.

The output of a clock circuit moves continually from logic 0 to logic 1 and back again. Electrically, logic 0 is represented by 0 V and logic 1 is represented by some higher voltage. If the clock runs at a low frequency, say 2 Hz, and its output is connected to the signal input of the oscilloscope, the spot will move slowly up and down between positions A and B, as in Fig. 14.11a, provided the time-base control is set to 'off'. If the clock runs at a higher frequency the spot will move so quickly that it will appear that a line joins positions A and B, as in Fig. 14.11a.

If now the time-base is turned on, the spot will move across the screen from left to right in addition to moving up and down. If the time-base is at an appropriate setting, the result is that a trace appears on the screen similar to that shown in Fig. 14.13. The time-base setting is found by trial and error. The trace is nothing more than a time/logic level graph drawn, not with a pencil on paper but, with an electron beam on the phosphor coated surface of a glass screen.

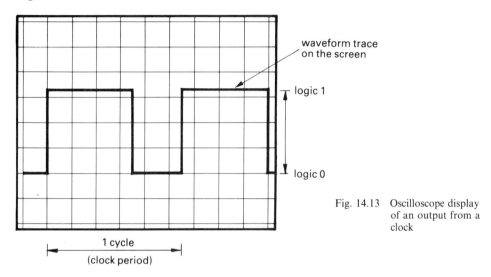

Fig. 14.13 Oscilloscope display of an output from a clock

From the oscilloscope trace, the clock frequency may be calculated. In Fig. 14.13, one clock cycle is spread over 5.5 divisions of the graticule. If the time-base control is set to 1 ms per division (ms = millisecond), one clock cycle takes 5.5 × 1 milliseconds. Therefore the clock period is 5.5 ms or 0.0055 s. The clock frequency in hertz is given by:

$$1/\text{clock period in seconds}$$

i.e. $1/0.0055 \text{ s} = 181.8 \text{ Hz}$

Before reading the number of graticule divisions occupied by a clock cycle, the horizontal position control should be used to move the trace left or right so that the vertical line at its beginning is aligned with a convenient vertical line on the graticule.

In addition to frequency, the trace shown in Fig. 14.13 allows the voltage level of logic 1 to be checked. Logic 1 is shown about 3.3 graticule divisions above logic 0. If the volts per division control is set to 1 volt/div, the oscilloscope is showing that the logic 1 voltage is 3.3 volts above the logic 0 voltage of about 0 volts. This is satisfactory for TTL integrated circuits.

An oscilloscope is connected to a chip under test by a probe which is at the other end of a lead which plugs into the instrument's coaxial BNC input socket, as in Fig. 14.11d. A good probe has a fine clip on its end which enables it to be attached to a chip rather than held in position by the user.

Dangling from the probe is a crocodile clip on a short length of wire. This is connected to the 0 V line of the system under test. The probe is connected to the appropriate pin of a chip. Great care must be taken to ensure that the probe only touches one chip pin at a time. It is very easy to short-circuit two pins by accident. Ideally, the probe should be attached to a **test clip**, as in Fig. 14.14. This fits securely on to an integrated circuit. Test clips are available to suit chips of different widths and with different numbers of pins.

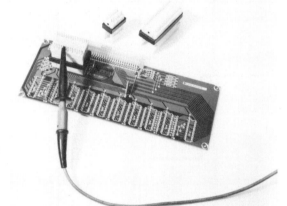

Fig. 14.14   Test clips

Other controls which may be found on an oscilloscope can include:

1 **brightness**. This makes a trace brighter or dimmer.

2 **focus**. This gives a trace with a sharp outline and no fuzzy edges.

3 **calibrate** or **CAL**. If fitted, the instrument will probably have two of these controls, one associated with the time-base control and another associated with the volts per division control. The calibrate controls must be in the CAL position if accurate time or voltage measurements are to be made. If measurements are not being made, the CAL control associated with the time-base control may be used to stretch or compress a trace horizontally. The CAL control associated with the volts per division control may be used to stretch or compress a trace vertically.

4 an **ac/dc switch**. When testing logic circuits this switch should be in the dc position.

As electronic systems, such as computers, have become more and more complex, it has become increasingly difficult to find and rectify faults. As a result, new test instruments have been designed. One such instrument is a **logic analyser**. At first sight, a logic analyser looks like an oscilloscope. It is able to tell a technician exactly what is going on in a system. However, the technician is left to understand the information presented and decide what to do with it.

Automatic test equipment, **ATE**, is a fairly new development which removes the need for interpretation by the technician. This is of great value as it enables complex systems to be tested with great accuracy in seconds rather than hours or even days.

15 CMOS

There are two main **families** of digital integrated circuits, **TTL, Transistor Transistor Logic** and **CMOS,Complementary Metal Oxide Semiconductor**.

☐ TTL Advantages

This book has concentrated on TTL chips. There are several reasons for this. TTL is the major logic family and is very widely used. New, improved versions of the chips are constantly being developed. TTL is ideal for the experimental work in the assignments. It is electrically robust, easy to interface to output devices and very forgiving if details are overlooked. For example, the inputs of unused logic gates can be left unconnected. This causes no problems as the internal circuitry of TTL makes an input **float** to logic 1. CMOS chips will not tolerate this treatment. All inputs must go somewhere. An unconnected input can make a chip or even a whole system malfunction.

☐ CMOS Circuits

CMOS digital integrated circuits offer the same range of logic functions as TTL as well as some additional functions. A circuit diagram of a CMOS logic system looks the same as the circuit diagram of a TTL system. A component list identifies which family of chips should be used.

☐ Code Numbers

CMOS logic integrated circuits belong to the **4000 series**. Most **code numbers** begin with '4' or '14' followed by three or four figures, e.g. 4001, 4508, 14002.

An exception is a range of CMOS logic integrated circuits known as the **74C00 series**. These chips have the same logic functions and pin-outs as the TTL chips with the same numbers but, in all other respects, they are CMOS chips.

☐ FETs

CMOS logic devices use **field effect transistors, FETs**, instead of the **bipolar transistors** used in TTL and the BC 108 and BFY 51 devices. FETs give

CMOS a number of distinctive characteristics. Some of these give CMOS advantages over TTL; others require CMOS chips to be used with care.

☐ CMOS Voltages

Most CMOS logic chips will operate from power supplies in the range + 3 to + 15 volts. Optimum CMOS performance is achieved with supplies of + 9 to + 12 volts. This is in marked contrast to the TTL requirement for a fairly exact + 5 V supply. It is one factor which makes it possible to use a dry battery to power a CMOS system.

☐ CMOS Current

Another factor is that CMOS devices draw only a minute current (nanoamps) from the power supply when quiescent, i.e. when not changing logic level. The current rises as a gate changes logic level. Even then, the current is still only a few microamps.

Because CMOS can be battery-powered, it is particularly suitable for use in portable equipment such as digital watches, digital multimeters and calculators. Many digital watches draw so little current that their small batteries will last for five years. Some calculators operate from the tiny amount of energy generated by a small solar cell.

The current drawn by a CMOS device varies linearly with its supply voltage. This means that, if the supply voltage is doubled, the current drawn is doubled. Even so, the currents are still very small. What is more important is that the current drawn also varies linearly with the frequency of logic level changes. For example, a clock circuit running at 1000 Hz draws ten times the current of a 100 Hz clock. As frequency rises, CMOS loses its low current advantage over TTL. In high frequency systems, TTL is better than CMOS because it uses less current and can operate faster.

☐ CMOS Logic Level Voltages

The logic 0 voltage level for a TTL logic gate input lies between 0 V and 0.8 V. The logic 1 voltage level lies between 2.4 V and 5 V but, in practice, might not rise above 3.3 V. These narrow voltage bands make TTL vulnerable to **electrical noise**. This can make a gate change logic level unintentionally.

The logic 0 voltage band for a CMOS logic gate working on a 5 V supply, is from 0 V to 1.5 V. The logic 1 voltage band is from 3.5 V up to 5 V. These wide voltage bands give CMOS devices the advantage of good immunity to electrical noise.

It essential that CMOS inputs at logic 1 are pulled right up to the supply voltage while inputs at logic 0 are pulled right down to 0 V. Near enough is not good enough. It causes loss of two advantages, noise immunity and low supply current.

190

The input of a CMOS gate, like a TTL gate, must make the transition from one logic level to the other very rapidly, in less than five microseconds.

☐ **CMOS Inputs**

A CMOS logic gate input is, in effect, one plate of a tiny capacitor. Its **impedance**, which for a capacitor is like the resistance of a resistor, is about one million-million ohms. This means that no current flows into or out of the input. This is quite unlike a TTL input which sources current.

One advantage of this is that a pull-down or a pull-up resistor can be connected to an input. Also, the resistor values can be high, e.g. 10K.

A disadvantage of high impedance inputs is that they can be destroyed by high voltage static electrical charges. These charges build up in such things as plastic laminates on bench work-tops and clothing made from nylon and other synthetic fibres. The charges cause the electric sparks which can be seen and heard when taking-off a nylon shirt or blouse. Manufacturers incorporate input protection circuitry in many CMOS chips. It consists of diodes and resistors and reduces, but does not remove, the risk of damage by static electricity.

☐ **Unused Inputs**

An unconnected CMOS logic gate input floats to half of the supply voltage. This makes the logic gate behave like a **high gain amplifier** and respond to electrical noise and radio signals. Supply current rises and the chip malfunctions.

Whenever CMOS logic chips are used, it is essential that all inputs go somewhere. Unlike TTL, *unused CMOS inputs may not be left unconnected.* They must be connected to logic 0 or logic 1 through a 10K resistor. One resistor can serve for all of the unused inputs on a chip.

☐ **CMOS Outputs**

CMOS outputs differ from TTL outputs in several respects. When a CMOS output is unconnected, or connected only to CMOS inputs, its logic 1 voltage level is equal to the supply voltage. When a TTL output is at logic 1, it is at about 3.3 V rather than the 5 V of the supply.

Unlike TTL outputs, which can only sink current, CMOS outputs can sink or source current. To sink current, a load is connected between the output and the positive supply rail. The load is energised when the output is at logic 0. This is the same as for TTL. To source current, a load is connected between the output and the 0 V rail. The load is energised when the output is at logic 1.

CMOS output current depends on the supply voltage. When operating from a $+5$ V supply, most CMOS outputs ought not to sink or source a current greater than about 0.8 mA. If a greater current is demanded, the output becomes increasingly unable to move down to logic 0 (to sink current) or up to logic 1 (to source current). This can cause great problems if the output has to control a CMOS input as well as drive a load.

The best way to get a CMOS output to drive a load is through an interface circuit such as the discrete component Darlington Driver or octal buffer, the ULN 2803A, used on the logic board.

Occasionally, published circuits show an LED connected to a CMOS output without a current-limiting series resistor. This practice is to be avoided as there are many pitfalls attached to its indiscriminate use.

The **fan-out** of a TTL output is usually 10. This means that one standard TTL output can drive up to 10 standard TTL inputs. By contrast, a CMOS output can drive up to 50 CMOS inputs. A fan-out of 50!

☐ Handle with Care

CMOS chips are dispatched from semiconductor factories in special antistatic packaging. They may be packed in antistatic tubes or clips or pressed into conductive plastic foam. The foam is black because it contains carbon — and is useful for making pressure sensors! Component suppliers sell CMOS chips either in their original packaging or pressed into pieces of white polystyrene ceiling tile which have first been wrapped in aluminium foil.

When CMOS chips arrive from a supplier, keep them in their protective packing until required for use. When using CMOS chips, work on a bench with a plain wood top. If a chip is to be soldered into its circuit, be sure that the bit of the soldering iron is earthed. Before removing a chip from its antistatic packaging, disperse any static electrical charge in your body by touching an earthed piece of metal — a cool metal part of the soldering iron, a metal electrical wall socket, a plugged-in electric kettle. Avoid touching the pins of the integrated circuit.

If chips are removed from a circuit, do not leave them lying around. Store them with their pins enclosed by antistatic material. Do not store them in white polystyrene ceiling tile without first wrapping the tile in aluminium cooking foil. Do not poke the pins through old holes in the foil. Always press the pins through an unpunctured area. The whole idea is to keep all of the pins electrically connected and all at the same voltage. It is when a static charge takes one input pin to a high voltage that the damage is done. Do not handle the pins of the chips.

☐ Other Details

1 A CMOS chip should not be removed from or inserted in a circuit while the power supply is switched on.

2 When wires from a CMOS input have to go off the circuit board to, say, a switch or a sensor, connect a 1M resistor on the circuit board between the

input and the 0 V or positive supply rail. The choice of rail depends on the switch or sensor circuitry.

It may appear that CMOS chips are fragile devices which are difficult to use. This is not the case as long as they are understood and a good working environment is maintained. Many of the more expensive but very 'clever' and useful integrated circuits use CMOS technology. Amateurs can use them successfully and without sad mistakes provided attention is given to their needs.

☐ Interfacing TTL and CMOS

Fig. 15.1 shows how TTL and CMOS integrated circuits may be interfaced so that combined systems may be produced.

Fig. 15.1 Interfacing TTL to CMOS and CMOS to TTL

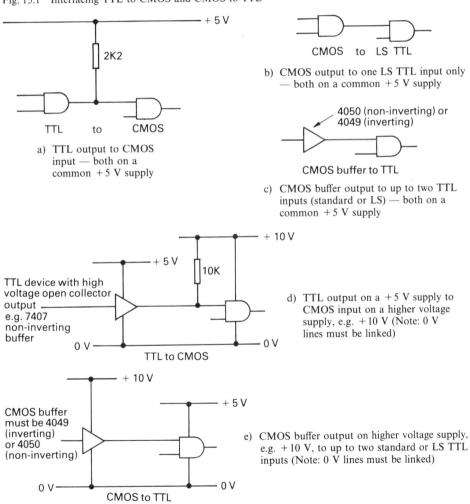

a) TTL output to CMOS input — both on a common +5 V supply

b) CMOS output to one LS TTL input only — both on a common +5 V supply

c) CMOS buffer output to up to two TTL inputs (standard or LS) — both on a common +5 V supply

d) TTL output on a +5 V supply to CMOS input on a higher voltage supply, e.g. +10 V (Note: 0 V lines must be linked)

e) CMOS buffer output on higher voltage supply, e.g. +10 V, to up to two standard or LS TTL inputs (Note: 0 V lines must be linked)

193

☐ Decouple

When a permanent system is built, it is important to decouple the power supply to the integrated circuits. 0.1μ low voltage ceramic capacitors are used. Use one capacitor to every six CMOS chips. Mount the capacitors on the circuit board and solder their leads to the 0 V and positive power supply rails as electrically close to the chips as possible.

16 Position Detection

☐ **Encoding Patterns**

Digital microelectronic systems are used increasingly to control machines. A part of a machine, e.g. a robot arm, may have to stop at any position between the extremes of fully up or fully down. If the control system is to stop the arm in the right place, it must know where the arm is at each and every moment. There are many ways in which positional information can be fed back to a control system. One of them involves the use of **encoding patterns**, as in Fig. 16.1.

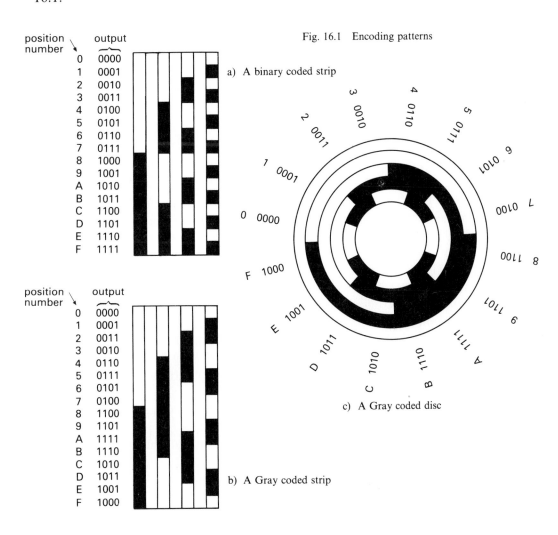

position number	output
0	0000
1	0001
2	0010
3	0011
4	0100
5	0101
6	0110
7	0111
8	1000
9	1001
A	1010
B	1011
C	1100
D	1101
E	1110
F	1111

a) A binary coded strip

position number	output
0	0000
1	0001
2	0011
3	0010
4	0110
5	0111
6	0101
7	0100
8	1100
9	1101
A	1111
B	1110
C	1010
D	1011
E	1001
F	1000

b) A Gray coded strip

Fig. 16.1   Encoding patterns

c) A Gray coded disc

195

Where the arm movement is linear, a printed strip can be made to move with the arm. The strip has a pattern of black and white markings set out in columns so that binary numbers are represented, as in Fig. 16.1a. White means logic 0 and black means logic 1, though the opposite convention may be used. If four columns are used, 16 numbers can be represented by the black and white pattern.

A stationary light sensor is fixed over each column of the strip shown in Fig. 16.1a. Each sensor responds to light reflected from its column. Each outputs a logic 0 or a logic 1 from its circuit, as in Fig. 16.2, according to whether it is over a white or black area. Together, the four sensors output a 4-bit binary number which changes as the arm moves. This information about the arm's position is input to the control system, which could be a computer.

A four column encoding pattern can detect 16 different arm positions. An eight column pattern has a better **resolution**. It can detect 256 arm positions.

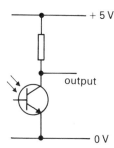

Fig. 16.2   A light-sensing circuit which uses a phototransistor

☐ The Gray Code

A serious problem with a **binary coded pattern**, as in Fig. 16.1a, is that it sometimes generates **false information**. If, for example, the arm is moving and is at its mid-position, the light sensors output 0111 and, a moment later, 1000. At the instant of change from one reading to the next, the sensors will always output 1111. For a moment, the control system will think that the arm is at the end of its travel. The result is erratic behaviour of the machine and this can have serious consequences.

The problem arises because, in the binary code, more than one digit can change in moving from one value to the next. Sometimes all the digits change, as in moving from 0111 to 1000. The **Gray code**, as in Fig. 16.1b, overcomes the problem because only one digit ever changes in moving from one value to the next.

Where angular displacement has to be detected, a Gray code pattern can be printed on a disc, as in Fig. 16.1c, or on a sector.

The encoding pattern need not be printed. Some alternatives are:

1   a slotted strip or disc;
2   a photographic image on transparent plastic or glass;
3   a series of cams with appropriate lobes which operate microswitches.

☐ Analogue to Digital Conversion

Positional information can be obtained from a **variable resistor**. The variable resistor can have rotary or linear movement. Its spindle or slider is connected to the part of the machine whose position is to be monitored. The basic circuit is very simple, as in Fig. 16.3. The variable resistor is wired as a **potential divider**. The output voltage, V_{out}, depends on the position of the spindle or slider and that, in turn, depends on the position of the moving part of the machine. This is known as an **analogue relationship**.

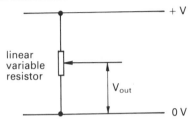

Fig. 16.3 V_{out} depends on slider position

The **analogue voltage**, V_{out}, is passed to an **analogue-to-digital (A to D) converter**. This is usually a single integrated circuit. The chip outputs a binary number which corresponds to the value of V_{out}.

Table 16.1 gives examples of the input to and output from an 8-bit A to D converter. The binary output is connected to the data bus of a microprocessor. This system is able to detect 256 positions of the machine part's movement. Other changing voltage sources can be input to an A to D converter, for example, the output of a heat or light sensing circuit.

Slider position (Fig. 16.3)	V_{out}	Binary number
Bottom	0 V	0000 0000
Half way up	1.25 V	1000 0000
Top	2.5 V	1111 1111

Table 16.1   Analogue input and digital output

Some A to D converters have several **analogue inputs**. Each input is known as a **channel** and each one could be connected to variable resistor connected to a different moving part of a machine. The microprocessor tells the converter which channel it wishes to read. The converter then puts a binary number on to the data bus. The Interpack interface has an 8-channel, 8-bit, A to D converter.

☐ Digital to Analogue Conversion

There are integrated circuits which work in the opposite way to an A to D converter. They receive a binary number from the microprocessor and output a corresponding analogue voltage level. These chips are **digital-to-analogue (D to A) converters**. A changing analogue voltage, suitably interfaced, could control the speed of rotation of a dc motor.

Index

198